Randy P.

OUT
of the
WILDERNESS

Young Abe Lincoln Grows Up

by Virginia S. Eifert

Author of "THE BUFFALO TRACE"
and "THREE RIVERS SOUTH"

Illustrated by MANNING DE V. LEE

BACK OF EVERY man is the boy he used to be, and behind every great man are the years which molded his character. OUT OF THE WILDERNESS is a stirring account of those early, almost forgotten years in the life of Abraham Lincoln, from which he emerged a heroic man. The book opens with the terrifying earthquake of 1811, which shook Kentucky when young Abe Lincoln was two years old, and it ends with the Winter of the Deep Snow in Illinois in 1831, when Abe was twenty-two. Between these dramatic events lie twenty years of growing up, adventuring, grief, joy, disappointment, hard labor and learning for the boy from the log cabin on Knob Creek.

The story is also very much that of a little-known man, Thomas Lincoln, Abe's father— the young, ambitious, prosperous Tom of the book's opening, and the embittered, hopeless man he had become when the story ends; and of the two staunch women who were his wives and who left their indelible influence upon his life and upon that of the growing boy, Abe.

OUT OF THE WILDERNESS is the third volume in Mrs. Eifert's Young Lincoln trilogy, which begins with THE BUFFALO TRACE, continues with OUT OF THE WILDERNESS, and ends with THREE RIVERS SOUTH, forming an absorbing, unbroken story. This carries the Lincoln family from 1780 until 1831 and is based carefully upon the few known facts of that virtually unrecorded yet vital period.

Virginia S. Eifert has always lived in Springfield, Illinois, the true Lincoln country, so her trilogy has developed naturally from her own background.

Again Manning de V. Lee has made many handsome full-page wash drawings, in perfect keeping with the fine text.

Ages 11-18

DODD, MEAD & COMPANY

OUT OF THE WILDERNESS

BOOKS BY VIRGINIA S. EIFERT

THREE RIVERS SOUTH
A Story of Young Abe Lincoln

THE BUFFALO TRACE
The Story of Abraham Lincoln's Ancestors

OUT OF THE WILDERNESS
Young Abe Lincoln Grows Up

GOING ADVENTURING OUT OF THE WILDERNESS

OUT OF
THE WILDERNESS

Young Abe Lincoln Grows Up

BY

VIRGINIA S. EIFERT

ILLUSTRATED BY MANNING DE V. LEE

DODD, MEAD & COMPANY · NEW YORK · 1961

LIBRARY OF CONGRESS CATALOG CARD NUMBER: 56-5488

Fourth printing

PRINTED IN THE UNITED STATES OF AMERICA
BY VAIL-BALLOU PRESS, INC., BINGHAMTON, N. Y.

This book is dedicated to my son

LAURENCE NOEL EIFERT

who, aged eight, accompanied me on many an expedition in search of young Abe Lincoln's background. Through the eyes and actions of a boy, I was enabled to see something of how another small boy may have climbed hill trails above Knob Creek valley and pitched rocks into Knob Creek's lazy waters, where fossils still lie embedded in the limestone; was able to see more vividly how another boy may have ranged the Indiana woods in search of an old beech tree humming with bees, or watched the alluring Ohio River flowing past.

Together, we traveled the route of the Lincolns from Kentucky, through Indiana, across the Wabash, and up into the Illinois Country.

Therefore, with my loving thanks for all his help and good companionship, I present *Out of the Wilderness* to Larry.

FOREWORD

THIS IS the story of how young Abraham Lincoln came out of the wilderness—the wilderness not alone of pioneer Kentucky, Indiana and Illinois, but the wilderness of the mind through which he struggled and from which he emerged to become great. It is the story of how he became educated without formal education, and of the people who were there when he needed them most.

ACKNOWLEDGMENTS

IN TRACKING down material and constructing it into the shape of a book which would eventually become *Out of the Wilderness*, second in the Young Lincoln trilogy, I am grateful to many people who have devoted time and thought to helping me.

In particular, I want to thank the librarians of Lincoln Library, Springfield, Illinois, especially Mrs. Audrey Major and Miss Lucille Fritz, reference librarians; Miss Margaret Flint, Illinois State Historical Library; Mr. Ora Brown and the late Mr. S. Grant Johnson of Dale, Indiana; Mr. and Mrs. Siegfried Weng, Mrs. Lee Kadel and Miss Claire Adler, all of Evansville and Newburgh, Indiana; Herman Eifert, for his critical help and encouragement; my neighbor, Mrs. N. E. Nilsson, for looking after things when I am away on book business; and Miss Dorothy M. Bryan, Dodd, Mead & Company, for her unending enthusiasm and help in making these books possible.

The general situation and many of the events and persons described in this book are based upon historical facts. However, the fictional characters are wholly imaginative: they do not portray and are not intended to portray any actual persons.

ILLUSTRATIONS

ix

CHAPTER ONE

T HE CLOCK on the mantelpiece struck twice, wheezingly, drawing in its breath after each thump as if to gather strength to go on,
and at the end, when the hour of two o'clock in the morning of
December 16th, in the Year of Our Lord, 1811, had been duly
announced, the clock's mechanism whirred frantically as if to re-
new itself.

The uneasy hour of two pressed around the clock with a darkness into which glimmered enough of a glow from the banked fire
in the big fireplace to cast a gleam upon the rough surfaces of logs
forming a big single room which was the Lincoln house. From the
roof poles at the kitchen end of the dwelling hung strings of dried
onions, a ham encased in a smoke-darkened cloth, and bunches of
dried herbs which, with the ham and the onions, gave off a faint
aroma in the chill of the room. The odor mingled with the scent of
the fire itself, made of good, long-lasting hickory cut on the Knobs
above the cabin, and the odors of a man's woolen clothing hung
over a chair-back to stay warm near the fire.

Suddenly, as the clock finished striking, Nancy Lincoln woke
up, her heart pounding with an unexplained fear. Something was
wrong. She always slept lightly, was attuned to listening for sounds
from four-year-old Sally and two-year-old Abe, but neither child
was stirring.

Wide-awake, Nancy listened for their soft breathing, while her
heart continued its frightened thudding. A little sound, a sound

which would have gone unnoticed during the day, now in the oppressive and menacing silence of night stood out loudly. It was a small, rhythmic tapping. Something—something was swinging back and forth, colliding with stones or wood at each swing. As Nancy listened, she became aware of a curious quivering sensation which was growing in the bed beneath her.

And then, with a silent crash, the whole bed, the whole room, the whole world shook violently. The clock stopped ticking, and Nancy half-sat up and leaned over hastily to shake Tom Lincoln's big shoulder.

"Tom, wake up! Tom—*Tom! Wake up!* Something's happened!"

Sally, wakening to terror, plunged like a scared rabbit into the big bed with her parents and burrowed under the covers. Abe, left alone in his trundle bed, opened his mouth and screamed.

Down the Cumberland Trail, winding through Knob Creek valley in northern Kentucky, other folk were being shocked awake to a night of fear. Caleb Hazel across the road from the Lincolns opened his eyes and lay trying to quiet his panic as the shock wave rolled under him. His dog was howling outside. Caleb Hazel sat up, let his lean shanks hang over the edge of the bed and felt with trembling feet for his moccasins. A man was better off, he figured, meeting death on his feet than in his bed.

Except for his dog, which was still keening at the door and scratching crazily at the oaken panels, he was quite alone. His son was in Louisville. His wife had died years ago and the stepchildren of that marriage were grown and gone. It was bitterly cold in the cabin. He lit a candle and peered at the clock, which had stopped at five minutes past two . . . a dreadful time of day for anything to happen. He unlatched the door, where the hound was still pawing madly, and the dog entered in a panicky bound, tail tucked between its legs, and cowered against him. Caleb Hazel's long fingers stroked the dog's head without any assurance in their touch.

"Go lie down, boy," he ordered, but without much conviction in his voice.

Caleb Hazel shivered. He stooped, bracing himself against the next shake, to poke up the fire. He opened the door and stepped cautiously outside into the winter darkness, but his dog, refusing to go with him, retired to cower under the bed.

Across the road, Caleb heard Tom Lincoln's dogs howling and his horses thumping and nickering in the barn; the cow was bellowing as if she had lost her calf.

Over in the blackness of the forest, on Bigg Hill, there was a moving point of light in the neighborhood of Tripoli Van Hook's cabin and the mysterious Stone House, and then, as another shake rattled Caleb's cabin, the light vanished.

The Stone House, Caleb knew, was a mystery which no one had solved. Built at the turn of the century, it had never been occupied, and its original owner had disappeared before the house was completed. If a man was out late on the Cumberland Trail, he often saw mysterious lights flickering in the vicinity of the Stone House, but people generally stayed away. There was some talk of ghosts. Boys in the neighborhood dared each other to go and climb into a window of the Stone House and see what was there, but even they were afraid to venture into the sphere of wrath of one Tripoli Van Hook, who owned the land and the Stone House with it, though he lived high on the hill, in a small, rough cabin overlooking the entire valley.

Nobody, Caleb realized, liked Tripoli Van Hook. He was small and silent and limping and fierce-browed. His head was as hairless as if he had been scalped, and it and his skin were brownish yellow, as if he had been deeply tanned by some tropic sun and had sickened with a fever which had yellowed the brown to an unwholesome hue. Tripoli wore a big gold hoop earring in the long lobe of his left ear, and the boys said that that was because he was a pirate. It made them even more hesitant of trespassing on pirate-owned land. They said Tripoli carried a knife and would slice off their ears.

More realistically, others talked of the bull whip he owned and recalled how he had flicked the great lash so that he cut off his enemy's clothing, sleeve by sleeve, pants leg by pants leg, ripped his riggin' to shreds and lacerated his flesh, before the constable clapped Tripoli in jail, and the doctor came to sew up the other man.

Caleb knew that Henrik Van Hook, a Dutchman out of New York State, had gone to sea to help fight the pirates off Tripoli, when the infant navy of the new United States of America had had to defend the rights of its ships to carry on trade in foreign waters. Henrik Van Hook had been among the nameless seventy-five men who went with Stephen Decatur to burn the American frigate *Philadelphia* in Tripoli Harbor, where it had gone aground and had been captured. When the valiant Decatur could not endure the thought of an American ship surrendering to the enemy, he and his volunteers ran a commandeered ketch into the harbor by night and set fire to the *Philadelphia*. In that pure release of the flames she would be free at last. The enemy, however, discovered the Americans at the moment when they swarmed over the sides of the American ship, and there was a brief fight, but the mission was accomplished. The ship burned. Decatur and his men escaped. Only one was wounded . . . Tripoli Van Hook, who carried a scar on his breast to show where a Moslem scimitar had gone for his heart, but had missed.

Van Hook came back with adventure behind him, came back to find his wife dead and his daughter vanished. Tripoli left his home on Fishkill Creek and traveled out to Kentucky. He lived all alone in a cabin overlooking the entire valley, where he could see all that went on, could count all who passed on the road, yet was unobserved in his aerie.

A rudely lettered sign board down near the main road said "Keep Out," leaving no doubt about the welcome awaiting rash adventurers who, uninvited, sought out the man at the top of the hill. If they did get so far—as young Austin Gollaher did one day, when he and Billy Mingus and Pelitiah Hill dared each other to see how far they could go before they were chased out—up in the yard there was a most terrible dog. Austin told about it.

The animal looked like part wolf, but worse than a wolf; at least, a wolf was self-respecting, a decent-appearing animal, like a big wild dog. But this thing up at Van Hook's, it had sort of humped shoulders, Austin said, and a smallish, misshapen head, with ears lopping over after they started to stand straight up, one ear flopping down as if broken in a fight. And the thing had such teeth! Austin shuddered at the memory of those teeth, and the way the animal barked and howled, as if it was sobbing or crying at the same time, worse than any wolf out on the hills in winter. And to top it, this humped, howling, hyena-like beauty was blotchy brown on moth-eaten gray fur.

"Never seen nothin' like it!" declared Austin. "Never want to have nothin' to do with it, neither!"

On the horrid night of December 16, 1811, with each set of unsettling shocks, the hyena dog was sobbing and keening dismally, worse than usually, and pretty soon, down the rocking path through the woods a lantern flitted toward the Stone House and then was invisible.

The shock wave, rolling toward the east end of the valley, struck a certain large brick house, which was suddenly full of commotion.

It was the largest and finest house in Knob Creek valley—big, to contain all the Montos, for Isaac and Sophia had produced eight sons, all living, all fully grown, all large, loud, emphatic men who said their say and argued trifles with gusto and enthusiasm. They indulged in rough-and-tumbles until the broad-planked floors shook, and their mother, a small, determined woman, smacked them with a piece of kindling wood. Then, laughing, they would all get to their feet and grab her up and hold her high, until her copper-red hair almost touched the ceiling.

"Let me down, you varmints!" she'd scream, but the boys would only laugh and make her promise to turn out a batch of griddle-cakes right now, this very minute, or maybe some molasses taffy, before they would let her down.

Sophia Monto always gave in. The stick of kindling was wielded to good effect when she really wanted to, and her sons let her whack them because they loved her and indulged her small tempers.

She adored every one of them, none of whom was less than six feet tall; and three-fourths of them wore heavy black beards and let their hair grow long. Sophia was small and neat and well held together. Only the twins, Amos and Abel, had inherited her crisp red hair.

Big Isaac, their father, could shout down the loudest of the tribe, which was usually Anse. It was a plumb noisy, rackety household, Sophia sighed to her neighbors, but she supposed she would feel the emptiness and silence and unbearable loneliness when the boys finally made up their minds whom they wanted to marry and set up homes of their own.

At the first shake of December 16th, a brick was knocked loose from one of the chimneys of the Monto house and banged on the roof. It slid down the clapboards, dropped to the ground two stories below and smashed into Sophia's precious little glass house where she grew vegetable plants for early planting. Both glass and bricks were rarities in the valley, and it was a point of some irritation among the neighbor women that Sophie Monto had glass enough not only for all the windows in the big house, but enough to waste on a cold frame besides, while most of the cabins in the valley had no glass panes at all, but were lucky to have oiled paper or hog membranes to let light into a window and keep out the wind.

At the first concussion, and at the sound of breaking glass as more bricks followed the first, the boys woke up.

"What in thunder!" cried Anse, leaping out of bed and groping for his breeches, but he got into Alexander's instead, and since Alex was thinner than Big Anse, they didn't fit. He yanked them off inside-out and found his own just as Alexander was fumbling with them.

"You stay out of my riggin'!" Anse snapped. "What you reckon's happenin', all that noise and this infernal shakin'?"

"Don't know," muttered Alexander, bracing himself to get his long legs into his breeches.

Red-haired Amos and Abel tottered sleepily to the door. Amos had a lighted candle. The twins leaned on each other's shoulders, yawning.

"What in time is it?" they mumbled, rubbing their eyes. "Thought we heard glass a-breakin'."

"Maw's cold frame!" shouted Abijah from his room.

"Chimney's fallin'!" yelled Jacob.

"Yow!" howled Aram, falling over a chair in the darkness. "Tarnation fool chair!" he yipped, rubbing his bare shin and groping for his shoes.

"Where-at is Maw and Paw? They all right? That there shakin' nigh threw me out of bed!" cried Arthur.

"Boys!" called Sophia in composure from the bedroom which she shared with Isaac. "Don't make so much noise! Get your garments on—and behave yourselves!"

Big Isaac climbed gingerly forth onto the cold, uneasy floor and dressed in silence. Every time a shake came, he sat down to keep from falling. Sophia appeared, fully clothed. A fresh cap covered her crisp red hair, which never lay down decently, but was like a thousand little copper wires, thin as gossamer, creeping out from under the prim white cap with the lavender ribbon.

The boys were all shouting at once. The succession of heavy shakes did nothing to abate the racket.

"Oh, shut up!" roared Isaac finally, his patience boiling over. "Quit your jawin'! Nothin's happened yet, 'cept'n the chimney's let fall some bricks and messed up Maw's cold frame, and the house is a-shakin' like all possessed. We're still alive, ain't we? Stop that infernal yellin' so's a body can think! What's the time?" The house rocked violently again. Abijah wondered why the time mattered.

"Five after two, Paw," said Amos, sniggering to Abel about how Paw had his boots on the wrong feet and didn't know it yet. "But the clock's done stopped, so there's no tellin' *what* time it is!"

"Heaven's mercy, what an hour!" cried Sophia, hand to heart.

"You keep still, too, Soph," ordered Isaac, in a foul mood. "You boys go see the horses is all right. I hear 'em nickerin' out there and thumpin' around like a panther's after 'em. See they don't hurt one another, kick down the stalls or harm that new black filly. Better look at the cows, too, and the rest of the stock, and go see what them fool hands is yowlin' about. Likely they're scared stiff by all this confounded shakin' and slidin' around. I never see the like

7

of it in all my days! Now git! And when you come back in, you bring that Molly woman and tell her to git vittles on. I'm hungry!"

On the hill southwest of the Monto farm, Jonathan and Sarah Joseph were awake, too. Sarah was trembling with fear, and with each shock she cried out wildly and gripped her husband until her nails dug into his flesh.

"I'm going to have a spell, Jonathan," she cried. "I know it—I feel it coming on! Hand me my elixir—there—now rub my head and then my wrists. Oh, that horrid shaking!" she wailed in mounting panic.

"Oooohhhh—whatever *is* it, Jonathan?" she babbled. "My heart —my heart—it's a-palpitating something awful. Hold the candle close and see if my eyes are getting glassy. Oh, I do wish you would ride in and get Doctor Potter to come out from town and bring me some new medicine before I die—"

"Now, now, Sarah, you just lay quiet," her husband soothed. "It's nigh twenty mile to town, and I couldn't go off and leave you, with all this shakin'. The house might fall in on you, and I wouldn't be here to get you out! Now lay quiet, honey, and I'll rub your forehead."

Jonathan was trying to sound reassuring, trying to surmount his own alarm, though his heart was in a panic as the unexplained shocks shook the house, and there was that dreadful feeling of an unstable earth shifting about under his feet. The shaking wasn't so bad; it was the way the floor moved under him.

Sarah Joseph enjoyed ill health and was unwell most of the time, a situation which she handled genteelly and with considerable relish, but this awful night was becoming too much for her, and she was close to hysterics. In desperation, Jonathan picked up her light body in his arms and, walking heavily back and forth with her, tried to soothe her fright.

Down in the valley, Job Dye was roused by his thin, dry wisp of a sister, Miss Emmarilla, who did for him since his second wife died. Wives wore out fast in the wilderness, but Miss Emmarilla looked as if she would last forever.

"Job, Job, wake up!" she cried in a thinly veiled terror which her stiff-necked pride would not let her show. "Somethin's happenin'—get up, quick!" She drew in her breath in a gasp as another shock struck the cabin, then straightened:

"This may be our last hour on earth, and you don't want you should be caught asleep and in your night-riggin'!"

Job opened his pouched, bloodshot eyes and, with a sick sensation, felt the bed slide and reel under him.

"Leave me be," he mumbled and closed his eyes again, fighting nausea.

Miss Emmarilla pounced on him in terror, and her hard, bony fingers dug in and shook him wide-awake.

"You get up, Job Dye!"

"What in the name of the Fiend is it, Em?" he mumbled sickly.

"The end of the world, more'n likely!" she snapped, relieved to see him awake. "I been lookin' for it for some time. Way folk carry on in these days of sin, it's no matter of wonder to me. Dancin' and frolickin' when they'd ought to be on their knees prayin'. Not goin' to meetin' and workin' on the Sabbath, and forgettin' the gospel between times. If I was a-doin' it," she flared, "I'd a-wiped out humankind long since and started afresh!"

"And you with it?" Her brother grinned blearily at her from the bed.

"There are some," she replied virtuously, "who ain't afeerd to meet their Maker! Get up, Job. The sight of you layin' there fair turns my stomach!"

She staggered with another shake of the house, went into her own room and, with a lighted candle close by, she knelt tremblingly by her hard bed. Feeling the floor rocking under her again, she bent her thin neck, gripped her scrawny hands, moved her lips slowly and read from the leather-bound, spotty Bible which she laid open before her on the bed.

Down at Mingus's, all five children were howling in a crescendo of screams. Lizzie Mingus's best dishes had all cascaded down out

9

of the corner cupboard and had smashed to bits on the floor. The excitable Lizzie was screeching like a bobcat. Peter let forth a stream of strong words as he was knocked off his feet. The earth shook again, the house rattled, and a saucer, which had somehow missed landing on the floor with the others, rolled deliberately to the edge of the shelf, poised there for an instant . . . and joined the rest of the pieces in a heap. Billy and Amanda and Julia and Rebecca and John Paul Jones Mingus, the baby, opened their mouths wider and howled louder.

Half a mile away on Pottinger's Creek Road, Zachariah Riney, the tall, spare schoolmaster who ran a subscription school across from Peter Atherton's distillery, leaped out of bed and threw open the door, letting in a gust of cold December air. Maggie, his wife, shivering with fright and cold, hurried to his side.

Zachariah Riney rubbed a nervous, bony hand across his gray, stubbly chin.

"We got to get outside so's the roof don't fall in on us," he muttered, as another quake shook him. "Get your cloak and shoes on. Move, woman!"

He hastily yanked on his breeches and boots, and threw on his heavy buffalo-fur coat. Zachariah and Maggie Riney, the latter fumbling with shaking fingers at her rosary and whispering broken prayers, hurried out into the starless night.

One tremor after another rippled under their feet, stopped clocks as far away as Boston, cracked plaster in Charleston, destroyed houses and killed people in Missouri and sank many boats in the Mississippi. Over in Tennessee, the land fell in and the river, rushing in to fill the great gap, buried a Cherokee chieftain and his bride, so the legends said afterward. But the roof of Riney's cabin did not fall in. When morning came and everyone was still alive and unharmed, Zach Riney vented his irritation with the elements and his aching bones on his slaves, who were too frightened to work. He whipped them all and felt better.

Back at the Lincoln cabin, when the shocks began, Tom Lincoln, suddenly awake, lurched to his feet, staggered across the room and got a candle lit, but its light gave small comfort. Little Abe was wailing. Tom swooped down, and picked him up hastily and thrust the crying child into Nancy's warm and loving arms. She enfolded Sally and Abe together and would defend them until she died.

Tom went out to quiet the horses and brought in the dogs when he came back. Shock after shock struck the cabin, struck it first of the houses in the valley because the shakes came from the west and rolled progressively eastward. There were quiet spaces between when Nancy and Tom felt that perhaps it was all over, but then the rattling and rocking came again, some of it hard, some light. After a gentle one, Tom would say, trying to be reassuring, though his legs felt trembly and his voice lacked boldness:

"There, that was a light one, just a chaser. Now maybe it's all over and we can get back to sleep," only to have another one hit hard and all but knock him off his feet. All the while, a pewter ladle which hung on the wall near the fireplace was moving back and forth like a pendulum—that was the rhythmic tapping sound which had so puzzled and alarmed Nancy just before the terrible shaking began. And every now and then there came a small, mouse-like sound . . . a piece of clay chinking breaking loose and rattling to the floor.

Nancy comforted the children and herself by praying, her head bent over theirs, quieting them by the very sureness and forced serenity of her voice:

". . . . for though I walk in the valley of the Shadow of Death, I will fear no evil. . . ."

Day broke grayly at last. Clouds covered the sky and a feeling of snow was in the air. Nancy got up and dressed. She looked out of the cabin, up the valley to where a pinkness showed in the sky, between the blue-purple distant hills, where the Cumberland Trail went to Louisville, and could not see anything amiss. Things looked the same as ever. But it couldn't have been a dream. . . .

"Tom," she said, when her husband came in from feeding the stock, though the cow refused food and continued to bawl monotonously. "Tom, go find out what-all it was. We couldn't have imagined it—it was too awful, and—" She broke off with indrawn breath.

"There it is again!" The cabin shook and the kettle jiggled so that water sputtered out of the spout and sizzled in the fire. But the shake was soon over.

There came a pounding on the door.

"Miss Nancy—Tom—you all right?" a big voice cried, a good solid hearty voice, at variance with the unsettling of the universe with each group of quakes. "It's been an earthquake! You folks all right?"

Tom threw open the door—or rather tried to. It didn't open very readily and he had to pull hard. It had been that way when he went out to feed the stock, but the last shakes seemed to have made it worse.

"Door's settled," said big Anse cheerfully. "Ours is, too. Got to rehang it when this is over, reckon. Maw's cold frame got busted. South chimney fell over. Never felt nothin' like this before, did you, Tom?"

"Come in and set, Anse," said Tom, relieved at seeing his sturdy neighbor, and breaking into the flow of hearty words from the big red-faced man with the black beard and mane of black hair hanging to his collar. "Take some coffee."

"Maw sent me to see how you folks'd managed," Anse told him, coming in. "Can't stay—that coffee sure smells good, though, Miss Nancy, and I would trouble you for a noggin. Thank you kindly," he went on, as Nancy poured out a noggin of the brown, steaming brew.

He was just lifting it to his whiskered mouth when another quake came, just a little one, but the coffee sloshed down his beard and on to his jacket front.

Anse let loose a couple of sizzling words that were hotter than the coffee, before he caught himself, remembering Sophia's decree on profanity in the presence of ladies. He looked apologetically at Nancy, set the noggin unsteadily on the table and forcibly restrained himself while the shake lasted.

Then he got to his feet hastily and gulped what remained.

"Tom, you come on out a minute and look at the road," he said, mopping coffee off his beard. "You'll excuse us, Miss Nancy. I want he should see the cracks in the road from this here earthquake, so's we can get it fixed afore the next stage comes along and maybe breaks an axle. Come on out."

Outside, he went on, soberly and a trifle apologetically:

"Tom, the road ain't really much broke up. Reckon a load of gravel'll fix it. That ain't what I wanted to tell you. It's this: last night one of our best slaves run off, that big buck who calls himself General Braddock. Gone, just like that, and none of the rest will pipe up where he is. Maybe they don't know. The earthquake's got them so crazy with fear anyway, they don't know which end their heads is on this morning. That Molly who cooks for us, know what she done did? Tried to make coffee in the water bucket and broke eggs in the skillet before she put any grease to it! Fool woman! Maw took over. Trust Maw to do it up right. Nothin' ever unsettles her. . . . Anyway, Tom, you be on the lookout for that buck. There been too many gettin' away lately. Got to get them patrollers on the job. They ain't been doin' a mite of good so far, seems like."

"Is the road broke up bad?" Nancy asked her husband at breakfast.

"No, not bad," answered Tom, his mouth full of corn pone and ham gravy. "Cracks an inch wide, though, every whichway. . . . Anse says one of their slaves run away in the night," he went on. "Says we got to get them patrollers workin' harder to round up slaves that's been escapin' lately. Riney lost one last summer, you recollect, and there's been two of the Montos' now, and Joseph's lost one, I hear tell."

"I know," said Nancy, drawing her level black brows down in a frown. "I wish they would all escape, Tom, I really do. It ain't right for a human being to be a slave to another. I can't bear to see the gangs of slaves taken along our road, chained and so hopeless and sad. I sometimes wish we lived farther from the highway, way out in the wilderness, so's the children wouldn't see. They ask me

13

questions—'why are those people chained like that?'—and I can't think of a proper answer."

"Oh, now, Nancy," protested Tom. "It ain't so awful bad. Most slaves are treated good, and if they run away, they got to be caught and brought back. It's the law."

"No treatment is good to a man who is a slave!" said Nancy Lincoln crisply, getting up to clear away the dishes.

CHAPTER TWO

When the upheaval was all over, it was found that there was little actual damage in the Knob Creek valley, there in northern Kentucky, a few miles south of Louisville. A log cabin is peculiarly well constructed to withstand earthquakes, and most houses round about were made of logs, all but the Monto house, and it was so well built that it suffered little except for the chimney and the cold frame.

Looking back on the terrible time, Nancy was thankful they were all alive, for word had come, finally, of the people who had perished in the terrible New Madrid earthquake. Frightened though the Kentuckians had been, they at least were still alive.

The Lincolns had moved from the Sinking Spring farm, up near Hodgen's Mill, to the Knob Creek farm in the spring of 1811. It was good land here in the valley, some of the most fertile land Tom Lincoln had ever farmed. Knob Creek rambled through a valley set in rounded, wooded hills. Through it, from east to west ran the Louisville-Nashville Pike, the Cumberland Trail. It was a busy road with people often upon it, coming, going, in the restless times when a nation was expanding westward and this was one of the routes they used to get to where they were going . . . west. The run off from the hills had deposited a rich layer of soil in the valley where Tom's crops of tobacco and corn did wonderfully well.

On a fine June day in 1812, when the earthquake was nearly forgotten, Miss Emmarilla Dye came calling on Nancy Lincoln.

Nancy was expecting another baby in August, and Miss Emmarilla gave her unasked opinions on the coming event.

"Yes, I say it's a pity, I really do, Mis Lincoln," Miss Emmarilla said in her high, nasal voice. Her thin hands fussed continually with the reticule hanging from her narrow waist and lying in the lap of her black calico gown, as she sat in one of Nancy's splint-bottom chairs. Nancy had made some switchel of molasses and ginger and cold water, and Miss Emmarilla sipped it genteelly.

"To bring another child into this sinful world is a great pity, I always say. Better the human race should die out than keep on the way it's goin'!" Miss Emmarilla took another sip and glowered at young Abe who had come plunging through the doorway with Sally after him, both screaming with laughter.

"Frivolous, frivolous," clucked Miss Emmarilla, making clicking sounds with her tongue and then folding her thin lips firmly together. "Like all of them, thinkin' only of frolickin' and forgettin' all about church-goin' and a righteous life. Well, I can only say, I'm thankful *I* never brought any children into this world of sin!"

"Do you really think that, Miss Emmarilla?" Nancy asked curiously, smiling a little, with that sparkling light in her face which always crinkled up her eyes and lit her features as if a glowing warmth were held somewhere within. "I wonder if you really do," she said, more to herself than to the spare, grim-faced woman sitting opposite.

Miss Emmarilla, momentarily caught off guard, set her noggin of switchel back on the table.

"Of course I do, Mis Lincoln," she said sharply. "And now there's talk of war, of all things. That's all women seem to be good for, bringin' children into the world to fight wars!"

"War?" echoed Nancy, startled. "But why should there be war? They've got the Indians pretty well settled, and the British got beat in the Revolution."

"There's never any matter of reason to have another war," went on Miss Emmarilla bitterly. "You just leave it to the men, though. They'll find a reason. When things get dull, they whip up a war just to make things lively for themselves, so they kin be heroes and such! 'Course, this one may not happen. They say the president don't want war, but of course, he's a Federalist and the Federalists all think they know best and won't countenance fightin', not even to save the nation. But I hear tell that, at the Congress, Henry Clay is gettin' mighty uppity and loud, fair runnin' the whole thing. Mr. John Randolph calls Clay and Calhoun and his gang the War Hawks, and he's fightin' 'em tooth and nail, they say."

"But why, Miss Emmarilla, why do they want war? I haven't been to Elizabethtown for weeks, I guess, and Tom's never made no mention of any war!"

"The British!" said Miss Emmarilla with a curled lip, as if she were speaking of rattlesnakes, horseflies and mice. "They say the British are attackin' our ships again and actin' too big for their boots. So we got to set 'em down a peg and show 'em America's big enough to stand alone on the high seas, as well as on land. And . . . but that's neither here nor there. I'll trouble you for another noggin of switchel, Mis Lincoln."

"Have you heard anythin' more about who the slave runner might be in this valley?" Miss Emmarilla went on, changing the subject, now that she had disposed of the coming war. "Too many slaves vanishin' into thin air. Can't be found, hide *nor* hair. They're bein' hid somewhere in this valley, *I* say. Job, he's captain of the patrollers, he says he's got to have more men under him, else he can never rout out whoever's hidin' slaves and helpin' 'em on to the north. Folk talk and say Job ain't doin' his business proper, but the poor man is—he's lost a slave of his own, and that ought to make him want to find out who's a-doin' it. Sins, sins, nothin' but sins in this world, amen," sighed Miss Emmarilla.

She got up to go, much to Nancy's private relief. The melancholy conversation was growing both wearisome and depressing on such a lovely day, when the scent of clover was warm in the sunshine, and the wild strawberries were dead ripe and fragrant as rich perfume along the road. She must send the children out to gather them before the fruits fell or the birds ate them. But Miss Emmarilla interrupted Nancy's revery.

"*Humm,* I do declare, there's the coach from Louisville and

Frankfort, and it's stoppin' out there in front of your house, of all things! Expectin' company?" she pried.

Nancy looked. "Oh, that's Mr. LaFollette, back from Frankfort," she explained. "He went up to the legislature and left his horse here in our barn."

Stout Josiah LaFollette stumped through the dusty grass and up to the Lincoln doorstep.

"Welcome back, Mr. LaFollette," said Nancy cordially. "Sit you down and I'll bring you a noggin of switchel before you start home. It's turned down hot today."

Josiah was plainly overheated and tired, but he was also worried.

"Where's Tom?" he asked. "Thanks, I will have somewhat to drink, and if you've somethin' stronger'n switchel, I'd admire to have it. Where's Tom?" he asked again.

"Tom's out in the north field, hoeing corn," said Nancy. "I'll send Abe out to get him. And I'm sorry, Mr. LaFollette, but Tom don't hold with strong spirits, and we haven't a drop in the house."

"I'd forgot," said Josiah, sinking into the chair just vacated by Miss Emmarilla Dye, who stood, spare and bleak, in the doorway, taking in everything.

Tom, perspiring in the June sun of Kentucky, came hurriedly up to the house.

"Whew!" he exclaimed, wiping his face with a cloth. "Hot out there. Sure makes the corn grow, though, so I won't complain. Howdy, Josiah. What's news up at the capitol?"

Nancy handed him a drink and gave some to Mr. LaFollette.

"News enough," sniffed Josiah. "They say Madison has done declared war!"

"War!" echoed Tom, sitting down heavily. "So they done it at last!"

"I been tellin' you and tellin' you they would," went on Josiah. "Them War Hawks up at the capitol, that Henry Clay and Felix Grundy and John Calhoun, they been cryin' 'War, war, war, we got to fight the British again to justify our honor!' So now we got war, and what we got to fight it with? No, they never thought of that. Henry Clay, he spouted out that 'The Kentucky militia could capture Canada unaided!' Huh! The Kentucky militia ain't been ready to capture anything bigger'n a rabbit since the Indians been chased out.

"Clay talks a-plenty, but who we got to *lead* our militia, if we do try to take Canada singlehanded, I ask you that? They say Isaac Shelby will do, old 'King's Mountain' Shelby who fought in the Revolution. He's too old, I say. We need young men. Most of the generals in the United States Army are Revolutionary War men, gettin' too old to know which end of a gun is which. All they been doin' since '87 is sit around braggin' about the battles they fought and which they all won singlehanded. Bah!" Josiah La-Follette glowered into his noggin, discovered it was empty, and silently handed it back to Nancy for a refill.

"Well, Mis Lincoln," put in Miss Emmarilla, first chance she had, seeing that no one was noticing her any more. "I guess I will be goin'!"

"Wait, Miss Emmarilla," said Nancy. "You can't walk all that way in this heat. Tom'll carry you home."

"Ride with him, the way Tom Lincoln's horses caper about?" snapped Miss Emmarilla. "No thanks! I walked when I come to call and walkin' I shall go back. When I'm too feeble to do either, I'll stay to home. I bid you good afternoon, Mis Lincoln."

"Gloomy critter, ain't she?" said Tom Lincoln when she was out of sight. "Now, Josiah," he resumed. "Tell me more about it. So Madison really declared war, did he? After all the talk of old Jefferson doin' his best to keep out of war, the little fellow really spoke his piece, did he? And now we're in?"

"We're in," said Josiah grimly. "Madison don't want war no more than the rest of us, but he's been pushed into it. And we ain't ready, Tom. That's what scares me. Our whole coast line, from Maine to the Floridas, they say, is wide open to attack. The Great Lakes are unguarded. Did you ever think of the amount of shore line lyin' between us and Canada, Tom? And I hear that the Indians in the Northwest Territory already are armed, waitin' word from the Governor-General of Canada, and he's only waitin' for word from the King. I tell you, Tom, they'll lick us sure, and we'll be right back where we were in '75, with all the long hard years of the Revolution come to naught. It makes me fair sick when I think of all the men who died to give us liberty. I was in it from Valley Forge to Yorktown, and I realize what it means. Poor General Washington would turn over in his grave, did he know."

"Well, but we got forts, ain't we?" asked Tom vaguely. His notion of geography and the location of forts was dim.

"Yes, we've got forts," Josiah replied wearily, resting his chin on his hand. "We've got Detroit, right at the door of Canada, with about a hundred men stationed there, I reckon, rusty from lack of practice and led by officers who've gotten lazy and fat. Fort Wayne's got eighty-five, I hear, and they tell me Fort Harrison's only got fifty men, and Fort Dearborn, right in the Indian country, only has fifty-three, and there's a garrison up at Michilimackinac, up on the lakes, I don't know how many. Few enough, that I'm sure. Those little forts are sittin' ducks, ready to be picked off one by one by the Indians and by the Canadians and British, whenever they get around to it. But that fool Clay screams 'War!' And he's got half of Kentucky and Tennessee echoin' it after him, like a pack of ninnyhammers."

"Looks like it'll be Kentucky's war," said Tom thoughtfully. "From what you say, the rest of the country ain't much interested. Maybe it's been too soon after the last one. I was in the militia a long time ago. We never got a chance to fight none, but I guess I could volunteer and maybe get to see a little action this time."

"Oh, Tom!" cried Nancy, aghast. "You're thirty-four! You leave fightin' to the young men!"

Tom knew he was a little too old to volunteer, but he thought about it a good deal when he went to Elizabethtown and saw the men being mustered in, lank, lackadaisical, quid-chawing men from the hills, clad in dirty buckskins, leaning languidly on their long, vicious, Kentucky rifles, propelling a stream of tobacco juice halfway across the street, plugging a mud-dauber at ten feet. It was laughable, too, to see the officers trying to get a little order in the newly formed companies of men who had enlisted for only sixty days.

Scantily trained, dressed in the clothes they enlisted in, and still toting their precious Kentucky rifles, two thousand mounted Kentucky riflemen were sent to the Illinois Country with old General Samuel Hopkins, in October, 1812. Their mission was to wipe out the Kickapoo and Peoria villages on the Illinois River.

"Well," commented Thomas Gollaher in injured tones, "when I joined up, man, I sure never enlisted to go and shoot at no Injuns. Thought we was a-goin' after the British, like at Trenton and Yorktown. But no, we was bein' sent along under an old fat Revolutionary War general who had a hard time gettin' off and on his own horse, over into the blamed prairies to rout out a bunch of Kickapoo that hadn't done nothin' to nobody—yet—and we sure didn't aim to be the ones to make 'em *want* to do somethin'!

"We done crossed the Wabash, right enough, and started ridin' into Illinois, when lo and behold, there in the distance that night, we seen a great awful fire ag'in the sky, and scouts we sent out come back and said the Injuns had set the prairie afire to keep us away.

"Well, we didn't need much more encouragement to do that very thing. Injuns *nor* fires wasn't our dish. Old General Hopkins and his officers, they ordered us to go forrerd, but we just up and said, 'Sorry, General, we're a-goin' home!'

"There was two thousand of us, mighty nigh, and not so very many officers, and they soon saw it our way. So, mighty sore about it, they just had to foller us, and we turned and marched back to the Wabash and come home again. And here I am, glad to be back!"

There was considerable talk that winter about how disgracefully the Kentucky militia had behaved over on the Wabash, but the men who came back weren't much concerned.

"If we cain't fight the way we-all wants to, we-all won't fight," was the drawling ultimatum of the Kentucky militia, who in their own way had fought to take Kentucky from the Shawnee and Wyandot, and no soft, old general who'd been too long away from the wars could make them fight in any way in which they didn't want to.

By the end of 1812, Detroit had fallen. Attacks on Canada by the Kentucky militia had failed. The attack on Niagara had failed. There were only a few bright spots in the year, very few indeed, considering the blithe confidence with which America and the hotheaded Kentuckians had thrown themselves into war. Still, America had done right well at sea, folk figured, looking back. In due time, the stories of sea battles came inland to Kentucky, and few, perhaps, delighted the Kentuckians as much as the tale of Captain Hull.

"There he was on the *Constitution*," old Ethan Gable would relate for anyone who was listening, "drawin' nigher and nigher to the British ship, the *Guerriere*. And them British guns was rakin' her, knockin' off this and that, and the gunners were lookin' around at Captain Hull, wonderin' when in tarnation he'd tell 'em to fire. But he just kept standin' there, watchin' them two ships comin' closer and closer. Then the situation was just right for the captain at last. He was finally suited.

" 'Fire!' he shouted, and as he said it, he bent over, and what would you think—his knee breeches done split from stem to stern, right when his ship was a-blastin' of the enemy! But whether he had decent riggin' on or not, it was his ship that won that battle!"

It was winter again along Knob Creek. Tom's crops were in, his hogs and sheep were fat and good, the cattle were healthy, and he had three sleek horses grazing in good weather on the fine green grass of his pasture. When the first cold spell came, and Tom, with Caleb's help, had done the butchering, Nancy filled the smokehouse with bacon and hams. Winter was closing down on the knob hills of the valley, and the trees were bare and feathery and cold against a winter sky.

Nancy was thinner and there were dusky shadows around her big dark eyes, and there was little color in her cheeks. Often, her eyes looked out of the window of the cabin, across the road and down a piece, and up to the hill above Redmonds' place, to the

"THERE IT IS AGAIN!" THE CABIN SHOOK AND THE KETTLE JIGGLED SO THAT WATER
SPUTTERED OUT OF THE SPOUT AND SIZZLED IN THE FIRE.

"THIS STONE HOUSE IS ON MY LAND; THEREFORE, IF YOU TAKE SO MUCH AS ONE STEP TOWARD IT, I WILL BULL-WHIP THE FIRST MAN TO DO SO!"

Redmond family burying ground. There was a little fresh grave there, still so new that no grass had had time to grow on it, though Tom had cut cedar boughs to cover it and make it look more comfortable for the winter. The new baby had been born in August, but though little Thomas came into the world well grown and a lusty-yelling infant, the heat of August and September was too much for him. It was a hard time of year for new babies. The flies were bad, and Nancy spent her days fanning the sick baby, trying to get him to take his food. Dr. Potter of Elizabethtown came out, after Tom in desperation went in to get him, but he couldn't do much.

The flies were still bad, and the heat still bore down, and one day little Tommy Lincoln simply gave up and stopped breathing.

Since Abraham Lincoln, Tom's father, had died from an Indian bullet in '86, Tom Lincoln had known no deaths in his family, and the death of his son hit him hard. He built a tiny coffin and lined it with cotton padding and a piece of white broadcloth. He had always been good at coffin making and had made a pretty good living from it in Elizabethtown, long ago, but he'd never thought to have to make one for his own child, the little one that was named after him, who was to carry the name of Thomas Lincoln down the years, for generations. Grimly he finished the coffin, and some of the neighbors gathered for the brief service which the Reverend Wood from the Baptist church spoke, meanwhile mopping the perspiration off his ruddy face and from where it was running down the creases of his neck.

Because there was no near-by burying ground, they laid the baby in Redmonds' plot, for Nancy hated having her baby put far away from her. Here in the valley he was born and here he belonged. She could see his hilltop from the house, and somehow it gave her a morsel of comfort, even though her arms were empty of the baby she had wanted and had kept so short a time.

23

CHAPTER THREE

Spring, 1814, came sweetly into the Knob Creek country. A shimmer of rosy color moved like a flush over the forest as the red maples bloomed with scarlet and gold tassels held high on the pale gray twigs. Before there was any sign of leaves on any trees, or any color other than the grays and browns of the winter forest, the seeds of the red maples formed pink and crimson keys which set a haze of red among the duller hues. Then the sugar maples bloomed, and whole trees were plumes of palest yellow. The beech buds stood up taller than ever, slim and brown, their scales spreading to let out fluffs of bloom and tiny, pleated new leaves. Shadbush and redbud splashed color on the hills, and dogwood became a flutter of white, as if drifts of the snowy bloodroot blossoms on the hillsides had taken wing among the trees. It was high spring on the Knobs . . . spring in Kentucky.

A fragrance of new, growing things filled the air, the scent of damp brown earth and ancient leafmold above which stood the flowers of the spring woods—the drifts of lavender phlox and the tufts of valerian, the white violets and yellow violets and purple violets, big and lush, the umbrellas of May apples and the fragile yellow of celandine poppies under the beeches. The hill above the Lincoln cabin was a flower bed, her own private flower garden, Nancy said with a smile, for she could see the blossoms from where she stood at the cabin door, could note from morning to morning how the colors came and went and changed, how a growing surge of green was coming to the trees.

The fields were mellow, the brown earth waiting for the seed, and Tom was busy putting in sweet potatoes and white potatoes and early garden truck. Frosts often came late in the valley, so he was waiting a while before planting his corn.

As spring blossomed, Zachariah Riney was growing more and more disturbed about the slave situation in the valley. He called a meeting of the slaveowners in the schoolhouse, across from the distillery.

"I tell you, neighbors, there's goin' to be trouble, bad trouble, if we don't find out what's happenin' to them darkies that's disappearin'. They vanish into thin air, but you know dang well they're bein' helped to freedom, and I aim to find out who's a-doin' it!"

"You're right, Riney," said Jonathan Joseph mildly. "I lost one slave a-ready, and you never know when there'll be another turn up missin', rate they're goin' off these days. My wife says she hears them mutterin' among themselves when they think she's asleep and I'm not around, and she says they're goin' to send another on his way soon. Don't know whose—may be one of mine, for all I know —but someone's goin' to lose him a piece of his valuable property pretty soon, or I'm mighty mistaken!"

"You got any notions where to start findin' this-here slave runner?" asked Aram Monto, standing tall above the other men, his legs wide apart and his big hands propped in his suspenders. "If you got any ideas who's runnin' off our property, show me the way and I'll go break his neck personal with my own hands!"

"Well, we got no call to use violence now, Aram, and you be sure to tell your brothers that. We can set the law to rights in this valley without resortin' to bloodshed," said Jonathan Joseph, his blue eyes wide with alarm as Aram scowled his wrathy opinion of slave runners.

"Well," tabulated Zach Riney on his dirty fingers, "there's Tom Lincoln got no slaves, nor Caleb Hazel, neither, and Hazel's been outspoken and loudmouthed about slavery right along; I'd go to suspectin' him. Old John Shepherd got no slaves, either, and that woman of his is the shifty kind; never know what she's up to."

Anse Monto broke in with a loud laugh. "Guess likely you ain't impressed with that Genessee Shepherd! Heard how she blistered you that time you went up there to borrow Old John's grubbin' hoe, and she called you a shiftless squatter not to have one of your own! Haw-haw-haw!" guffawed Anse.

Riney squirmed and scowled. He pursed his lips and sucked his yellow teeth. "The woman was coarse and rude," he said righteously, "and I certainly won't go there for aid in distress. My wife broke her hoe and needed another'n to get the weeds down after the rain."

"That wasn't all she said to you, though, was it, Riney?" Big Anse asked with a meaningful grin. "Seems like I hear tell of her sayin' you ought to be ashamed lettin' your wife, frail as she is, work in the fields with a hoe on a hot day, or any other day, when you got slaves, didn't she now? Said Maggie Riney was mighty nigh the only white female in the valley who had to get out and work in the fields. No wonder that Genessee skinned your hide off and nailed it to the fence!"

Riney changed the subject. "The matter before us, gentlemen," he said distinctly, pointedly ignoring Anse, "is to try to find out who is runnin' off our slaves to the north. We named Hazel and Lincoln and Shepherd. Now we shall go on," he said in his best schoolmaster's voice. "I'd suggest Peter Atherton, too. His daughter Polly's sweet on Hazel's son, and you know the sayin', 'like father, like son.' And there's Daniel Vittetow and George Redmond, and Josiah LaFollette, outspoken as anythin' about slavery, like as if it was somethin' wrong; any of them could be the one. The rest of us have our slaves and we want to keep them."

"You're right," Anse Monto agreed. "All we want's to save our property, which we paid good money for. . . . You forgot one more in the valley, Zach," he added suddenly, "and that's old Tripoli Van Hook!" The others grinned with Anse when he said it, because Tripoli was a joke and everyone knew the man was crazy, not enough sense in his head to run off slaves, or reason to want to.

The next day, however, none who attended the meeting felt like grinning.

Jonathan Joseph, who seldom lost his temper, not only was not grinning, but he was downright angry. No man likes to have his belongings stolen out from under his nose. Slaves cost good money; he needed them to help run the house and farm. It was time for action, and he was going to organize that action now. One of his best slaves had vanished in the night.

The men gathered at the Montos' house, at the east end of the valley. Six brothers were at home; Alex and Abijah were serving their turns with the militia and were still down south somewhere, helping Andy Jackson win the Creek War. The remaining brothers, with their father, Isaac, were eager to get started on the hunt for the slave runner. Action always delighted a Monto. Job Dye was there, the patroller, trying to organize the crowd into the semblance of a law-abiding group on a legal mission. Old Thomas Hill was there, and cocky Tom Gollaher, sober Peter Mingus, and the sour schoolmaster, Zach Riney. Some had long, wicked-looking Kentucky rifles cradled lovingly in their arms. Job Dye had a big bull whip; the Monto twins had great hickory-wood clubs, strong enough to knock down a charging bull.

"Come on, let's go!" yelled Aram Monto. "I'm all for searchin' this whole blamed valley. We won't stop till we've found what we're lookin' for, I'm tellin' you that! Come on!"

Fired by Monto zeal, they all set out, west through the valley. The hunt took quite some time. All that day they searched house after house, into smokehouses, into storm cellars, into lofts and barns, hastily poking pitchforks into haypiles, finding nothing. The resentful but silent people of the farms so investigated let the men do as they wished, all but Caleb Hazel. He met them at the road in front of his place.

"Stay back, friends," he said pleasantly, but firmly, a steely glint in his green eyes. He stood his ground. "One step on my property and I will not answer for the consequences. You'll have to take my word as a gentleman that no slaves are hidden here, nor ever were. But if you insist on searching my place, which will mean that you think me a liar and hence no gentleman, come back decently with a search warrant!" And Caleb stared them down. Finally, they backed up, muttering.

"All right, Hazel," said Job Dye, growling. "We'll take your word for it. But if we can't locate what we're huntin' for in this here valley, and if we find the slightest reason to think you might be the one, we'll come back with that warrant, and we'll take your place apart till we find what we want!"

The crowd surged angrily across the road to the Lincolns' place. Tom Lincoln was in town. Nancy, white-faced, met her neighbors at the door.

"What do you want?" she cried, her hands twisting in her apron.

"Now, Miss Nancy," began Aram Monto gently, not roaring. "All we want to do is look in your barn and smokehouse and loft, to make sure there ain't no slaves hid here."

"I'm right sorry about this, Miss Nancy," said Anse, stepping up beside his half-apologetic brother. "We sure don't suspect you and Tom in this. Tom was a patroller himself long enough for us to know he's in sympathy."

"You're wrong, Anse," said Nancy firmly, looking at him with those level gray eyes of hers. "Tom was a patroller before we were married. I do not hold with human slavery, nor ever will!"

Anse took a step backward and Aram looked confused.

"Bravo, Nancy," said Caleb Hazel quietly from behind them, where he had been standing listening. The men, having found nothing about the place, were gathering again.

Young Abe came running up in great excitement. "Mammy, what're they lookin' for?" he cried.

"They think we've hidden slaves from them," she answered distinctly. "But you know that isn't true, don't you, Abe?"

"Sure, Mammy," he declared stoutly.

"Say, Mr. Monto," he added, "can I go with you to the next place and help you hunt?"

"No, Abraham Lincoln, you'll stay right here!" cried Nancy sharply, her patience worn thin. "Please go, gentlemen, before you've entirely ruined my son!"

"I'm sure sorry, ma'am," pleaded Anse Monto. Jonathan Joseph uncomfortably apologized for entering her house and barn. The men went out to the road again. Their enthusiasm was waning.

"Well, where next?" asked Aram glumly. He hadn't exactly enjoyed the way Nancy Lincoln's level eyes had bored into him.

"*I* say, go see what's in that there Stone House nobody knows anythin' about!" cried Zach Riney triumphantly. "We've always stayed away, since the signs made no mistake about our welcome. But now, I say, let's go see what's hidden there! We'll rout out old Tripoli Van Hook and see what he's got to say for himself!"

There was a roar of approval which sent a chill over Nancy Lincoln. This was more like it, the men agreed; action, not this miserable business of scaring women and children and searching the property of neighbors who would be offended for life. No one liked old Tripoli Van Hook; he was fair game.

The men swarmed down the road. It was getting late. The west end of the valley always grew dark before the sun had set on the eastern hills, because the forested bulk of Bigg Hill, blocking the valley, shut out the sunlight while it was still late afternoon. Shadows were deepening in the dark ravines past which the winding, tortuous road climbed to the top. The men turned into the stony little trail and surged as quietly as big men can go through the woods, to the brown mass which was the stained limestone walls of the Stone House. Its blank, glassless windows looked out without expression. There was only the reflected light of the sky, and the scent which limestone gives off as dew forms upon it, and no signs of life except the monotonous chanting of a vireo somewhere in an oak, until the hyena dog cut loose.

The dog must have been on its way down from its master's cabin, because suddenly the men saw the strange mongrel, fur bristling on its misshapen shoulders, teeth bared, broken ear at variance with the other, lolloping down the trail toward them. Behind it limped Tripoli Van Hook. His bare head shone grotesquely yellow in the shafts of late sunlight coming through the trees, sun sparks catching on the gold earring. In his hand he brandished a mighty bull whip with a lash nearly twenty feet long.

"Hola, Hans," he grated at the dog, which fell back to his side, snarling, but obedient.

"Now, gentlemen, I tell you once more and finally," he began patiently, "this is my property. You will stay off. Off! I say it again—off! This Stone House is on my land; therefore, if you take so much as one step toward it, I will bull-whip the first man to do so!"

He flicked the wicked lash and snapped a twig off an oak tree above the head of Jonathan Joseph, who stepped back quickly. The lash cut into the dust and whisked like an angry snake around the ankles of the intruders.

"All right, Van Hook," growled Zach Riney, well in the rear of the group. "You don't have to act like that. All we want is to see the color of what's hid in that Stone House. Folk say they've seen lights here at night, and I for one aim to find out what-all's inside, and why you're so anxious to keep us out! We've searched all the farms in the valley and haven't seen hide nor hair of our missin' slaves. They've gone somewhere! And I say it must be here they stay till they can be passed on up the hill to the next place! Stand aside, Van Hook, we're goin' in!" Zach Riney spoke big, but he kept the wall of the Montos safely between him and the bull whip.

"No," said Tripoli Van Hook, quietly, and the whip curled itself above the tall Montos and the lash laid itself about Zachariah Riney's head and left a bright red welt all around it. Zach yelled, clutched his head, and retreated a distance down the hill.

No one was very sure what happened after that. The men charged the stocky little figure of Tripoli Van Hook with his deadly whip, a shot rang out, a Kentucky rifle smoked, someone groaned, the dog sobbed like a werewolf, and a clear voice cried:

"Stop! Stop!" A thin, colorless young woman stood on the hill slope above the Stone House, looking down on the melee below. "What have you done? Oh, *what have you done?* Father!" Then she was down the slope and on her knees beside the crumpled figure of Tripoli Van Hook, whose hyena dog was slobbering its inarticulate grief upon his lifeless hand. The gold earring lay limp in the dust, dangling from his long lobe. Tripoli Van Hook was dead. But so, too, was Jonathan Joseph.

Caleb Hazel came on the run up the hill.

"So you had to use violence, after all!" he raged. "You had to kill to satisfy your blood lust. Look at you! Murderers! That's all you are!"

Aram Monto was staring dully at the two men on the ground.

"I did it," he mumbled. "I shot them—I didn't mean to."

"I only heard one shot," said Caleb tersely, down on his knees beside Jonathan Joseph. There was no mark on him. "He wasn't shot. What happened?"

No one knew.

"Someone ride to town and get Doctor Potter, so we can make this legal. Better get the sheriff, too." Caleb got to his feet. He went to where Tripoli Van Hook lay, the weeping girl crooning over him. The dog snarled as Caleb approached.

"Please, ma'am," said Hazel gently, "let us take you back to the house. You lived up there with—him?" Caleb Hazel was looking at the girl and she gave back a level gaze.

"She's the female who got off the stage the day Josiah LaFollette come back from Frankfort to tell us war was declared," remembered Aram in a subdued voice. "I recollect."

"I am his daughter," she said simply, not looking at Aram, but addressing herself only to Caleb Hazel. "My father . . . was not always himself. Terrible things have happened to him and his mind sometimes . . . but he is gone now . . . it is over . . ." Her voice trailed off thinly.

"Was he the slave runner?" bluntly spoke up Job Dye.

"My father felt very strongly about the rights of man," Greta Van Hook replied with dignity and pride. "He believed that all men should be free. You may look in the Stone House. No one is there now."

Nancy Lincoln was terribly disturbed by the whole horrid hunt and by the deaths of the two men. When Tom Lincoln came home from Elizabethtown the next day he was shocked at what had gone on in his absence, and, Nancy suspected, sorry that he hadn't been in on the excitement. He rode down to the Montos' at once, to find out more of the details and inquire about Aram. He found

Sophia Monto grim, dry-eyed, and tight-lipped.

"He's got no more than he deserved!" she snapped at Tom when he asked about Aram. "That I should ever live to see the day when one of my boys is hailed into court, but I've feared this many a time! They're all too hotheaded. It's a wonder to me they haven't killed someone before this, let alone each other. Now he's got to take the consequences!" But there were tears very close to spilling out of her frightened blue eyes.

Tom laid his big hand over her two nervous ones. "Now, Miss Sophie, don't take on," he soothed. "Aram ain't done nothin' so terrible—"

"Killing a man isn't terrible? Tom Lincoln, it's the worst crime a man can do, and the eyes of the Lord are upon him!"

"No, what I mean is, he didn't do it with malice aforethought. He got excited, as I hear it told, and when old Van Hook got to swingin' that bull whip, and they all tangled at once to take it away from him before he peeled the riggin' off them, Aram's gun went off and old Van Hook happened to be in the way. It could have been someone else, just as easy. And you can't blame Jon Joseph's death on Aram. Doc Potter says he died of heart failure. Aram hadn't nothin' to do with it."

"I blame every man who was there!" cried Sophia Monto, her wiry red hair bristling away from her face and her eyes snapping. "I don't care if we lose every slave we ever had, no man has a right to go out and cause the death of another man, just to recover his own property. It'll give the valley a bad name; and how're you going to explain things like that to your young ones, especially that sharp Abe and the questions he's bound to ask?"

"Well, I don't know, rightly," admitted Tom. "He was at me hard and heavy the minute I got home, tellin' me this and askin' me that. I only wish I had been home when all this here happened."

"Yes, so's you could mix into it, too," cried Sophia. "Lucky for Nancy Lincoln you weren't. But what's going to happen to my boy, Tom? Think likely they'll clap him in jail? Or hang him?"

"Now don't git excited, Miss Sophie," begged Tom. "Aram'll get out of this; he'll plead it was an accident and the judge'll let him off. I've been on enough juries up to Elizabethtown to know how the law works. You wait and see, and don't worry."

Sophia folded her lips in a straight line. "I'll wait to see justice done, and nothing else!" she snapped.

Justice was done. Aram Monto was hailed into court, his case was tried, and he was dismissed with a verdict of not guilty. But Aram and his brothers were considerably subdued for a long time after that, and Aram had a hard time making his peace with his mother months after everyone else had forgotten the matter.

As for Sarah Joseph, widowed by Jonathan's untimely death— Sarah blossomed. With Jon no longer there to care for her, she gained in strength and health, and a year after the two deaths near the Stone House, Sarah Joseph married again and went off to Louisville to live.

Tom Lincoln, however, had other things to think about. Slave troubles were bad enough when a man was burdened with enough wealth to spend some of it on Negroes to work for him, but when a man stood to lose his land, his most precious possession, then it was getting too serious to be taken lightly.

It was in 1813 that he had finally lost the title to his Sinking Spring farm, the 348 acres on the South Fork of Nolin Creek where Abe was born and where the Lincolns lived for two years. The land was gritty and rough, not as fertile as that in the bottoms of Knob Creek, but Tom held on to the property when they moved. It had made him feel pretty good to consider that he now owned 816 acres of good Kentucky land—farms at Mill Creek, Sinking Spring, and Knob Creek. That, perhaps, was the moment when Thomas Lincoln was most prosperous and affluent.

Then something happened. Never again in his life would he own so much land.

In the early days of parcelling out land in Kentucky, it was often done carelessly, so that titles overlapped, one on another, and sometimes another on top of that, until the first owner asserted his rights, declared all later claims null and void and took over his property. That is what happened to Tom Lincoln's farm. It was

33

confusing, and trying, and it ended in having money refunded all around—or so ordered by the court. Tom Lincoln, for one, never received anything as a refund, only a rising tide of bitterness which began to discolor his life.

Therefore, it was with a fear of losing even more of his land that Tom Lincoln, on that April day when two men died in Knob Creek valley, went to Elizabethtown to call at the Hardin County courthouse and take out the deed to his Mill Creek farm, north of Elizabethtown—238 acres on Mill Creek. Tom decided to sell that now, before he lost it, too, through the same discouraging litigation which had snatched the Sinking Spring farm from him. He found a buyer in Charles Melton, who paid hard cash for 200 acres. Tom discovered unhappily that, in selling it, he had lost thirty-eight acres, simply because the surveying line had been put in wrong.

"Kentucky may be beautiful," he later told Nancy, "but it purely snatches a man's land right out from under him!"

CHAPTER FOUR

A YEAR LATER, when Abraham Lincoln was six years old, he started to school. It was a subscription school and expensive, three dollars a month, but Tom Lincoln had the money and he wanted his children to have at least a little learning. Abe had pined to go with Sally the year before, but he was still too young. However, his mother said that six years old was exactly old enough, and Abe, in sheer delight, trotted the two miles up the road with Sally, to Zachariah Riney's school in the log house across from the distillery.

Somehow, though, the sight of the paunchy, scrawny, irritable Mr. Riney waiting for them with the school bell in one hand and a long, strong, hickory whip in the other took some of the joy out of the finest autumn morning.

"You're late again!" he'd snap. "Get in there and sit yourselves down. Don't let me hear a peep out of you young ones till I say so!"

Although he didn't much like Zachariah Riney, Abe Lincoln did manage to learn his letters and to read a very little. Painfully spelling out the words until they suddenly came clear and made sense gave him a wonderful feeling of accomplishment, so that he went home one day and proudly announced:

"Mammy, I learned to read today! Listen to me read you a piece!" It seemed almost like magic to make words come alive like that.

And Tom and Nancy sat down and listened to Abe haltingly read a few simple sentences calculated to instill morals as well as learning into the very young. Caleb Hazel had loaned Abe the

35

book, since he had none of his very own.

It felt good to read, but Abe was, besides, deeply curious concerning everything he saw or heard about. He did not take things for granted; he was obsessed with wanting to know—to know the names of the wild things he saw, to understand why doodlebugs acted as they did, why a wood thrush built one kind of nest and a redbird another, why dogtooth violets bloomed in spring and why wild asters waited until fall, and why there were curious prints in the rocks of Knob Creek. There were so many things he wanted so badly to learn, and Mr. Riney at the schoolhouse dismissed them as nonsense, or worse, when the boy brought in a strange-looking stone, or a new kind of insect, or the curious mushrooms he found on the hills. One day he showed Zachariah Riney a piece of limestone with a sea shell printed neatly upon it. The man snatched it from him and flung it out of the open door.

"That's the mark of the devil!" he shouted at the bewildered boy. "And you leave all suchlike things alone, hear? Learnin's to be had out of books. Now sit yourself down and do six more pages of cipherin' for punishment!"

But after school the thin, lanky, sun-tanned boy hunted around and found the piece of rock which puzzled him and hid it in his pocket. When he went home that day he stopped at Caleb Hazel's house. He knew he ought to have taken it there in the first place, but somehow it seemed to him that the schoolmaster ought to know the answers to things. That was what he was for.

"Mr. Hazel," Abe began, hesitating after what Mr. Riney had said to him, holding out the offending piece of stone. "Mr. Riney says this-here is the mark of the devil. Is it?"

Caleb Hazel held the piece of limestone in the palm of his calloused yet sensitive hand. His eyes smiled down at the anxious boy.

"No, Abe," he said gently. "I wouldn't say it was the mark of the devil. I'd say, rather, that it was the handiwork of God, a proof He has set down there in the rocks of our creek and round about to show us that His presence is everlasting. Abe, you've found what they call a fossil. They say that long, long ago there was a sea here, a real ocean-sea, with shells and creatures living in it, like snails and mussels live in the creek now. Somehow, the bottom of the sea turned to stone and everything on it turned to stone, too, or else left prints. Don't let Mr. Riney confuse you, Abe. He means well, but his eyes see only what's in books. You train your eyes to see everything that's around you, as well as in books, and you try to find out about everything you see. A man can read a lot of books and he can study spelling and learn to read and how to cipher, but his learning isn't worth much if he can't distinguish between the handiwork of God and the sign of the devil. It's a pretty fossil, Abe. Come on, let's go across to the creek and see what else we can find."

And Nancy Lincoln had to come to the door and call three times before Abe finally tore himself away from the fascinating discoveries he and Caleb were making in the creek. To the boy, it was one of the most exciting days of his life, almost as thrilling as the day when he had discovered that words on a page could be read and that, in learning to read, the world was opening up before him.

CHAPTER FIVE

From the long face on Tom Lincoln, Nancy thought, watching her husband riding dejectedly down the road from town on a raw March day in 1816, you'd decide he had lost his best friend—or his best horse, which would have been even worse for Tom. She went out to the barn and waited for him to come in and put the Red Duke to bed for the night. The Red Duke was a fine stallion which Tom had bought from his brother Mord not long before. The Duke was a descendent of Duchess, the red mare which Tom's father, Captain Lincoln, rode to Kentucky in 1780. The Red Duke was like a member of his own family, Tom felt, almost blood kin.

"What's the matter, Tom?" Nancy asked gently, when he had finished at last. She put out her hand to meet his, but he did not see it.

"Matter enough," Tom grunted. "It'll keep. I'm mighty hungry and it'll fair spoil my appetite to talk about this here piece of business if I start on it now."

Abe came in, muddy to his knees from playing in the soft earth. He and Austin, Billy Mingus and Sally had been digging a cave in the side of the hill, and Abe was dirt from head to foot. Nancy sent him out to wash his feet and his hands and face; she brought out a basin of warm water and some soft soap. Sally had some mud on her, too, but Sally could play as hard as Abe, yet always manage to come in fairly clean and neat. Not Abe! He was always the dirtiest of the lot, Nancy sighed, and could get into more scrapes, come home with the biggest set of bruises, the bloodiest cuts, the deepest scratches and the most cheerful face she ever saw.

Anything that happened was adventure to Abe, and it kept his mother on tenterhooks half the time, wondering what-all he was going to do next—like walking across the barn rafters, barefoot, or climbing the tallest tree on the highest knob hill, so he could see farthest, pretending to be a pirate on the Spanish Main, sighting a ship. The cave in the hillside was Abe's idea, too. They had looked for real caves, ready-made ones, after Caleb Hazel had told them about the big cavern a little way south of there, down in the Sinks country, where likely the biggest cave in all the world had been found at the turn of the century. A man named Houchins, Caleb had recounted, was out hunting one day and sighted a bear. The critter started up and ran toward the hill—much like these knob hills, Caleb assured the boys—and when Houchins got there, the bear was gone, hidden in a great black hole in the side of the hill. Later, the hunter and his sons had gone inside with torches and found wonderful rooms and passageways hung with crystal.

Fired by all this, Abe and his friends had hunted for a cave, but they couldn't find a hole in a hillside which led anywhere that amounted to anything, so Abe decided they might try digging a cave under a limestone ledge that would make a roof and keep it from falling in. There was always the hope, as they dug, that they might break through into a real cave, or even a treasure cave full of jewels and gold . . . you never knew.

Nancy tried to make conversation at supper, but Tom wouldn't talk. He applied himself doggedly to his food, shoveling it in in silence. Abe was busy chattering at a great rate about the cave, with Sally chiming in with him.

"You young ones shut up!" Tom snapped, finally. With a warning look, Nancy laid a hand on Abe's arm, and the children subsided, ate in silence and got up as soon as they were finished.

"Go study your lessons," said Nancy, and the two settled down by the fire.

"All right, Tom," she said at last. "What is it?"

Tom looked up. "We're bein' evicted," he said dully, with no more ado.

"Evicted? Why—that means bein' put off the farm! They can't do that—we've kept up payments, took care of the place, improved it, we're gettin' our fields planted. They can't!"

"Yes, they can," said Tom stubbornly, his big face frozen in discouragement and impotent, helpless anger. "Blasted Kentucky land! Can't count on nothin' any more. Man thinks he's secure, got good land and a house, and then he finds his title's no good and he loses everything . . . not once, but over and over. I've a mind to leave Kentucky to them as wants it, and go someplace where the land titles is safe and a man knows his boundaries—and knows they can't be took away from him!"

"You might as well tell me all about it," Nancy said hopelessly, letting her work-roughened hands fall into her lap.

The children looked from one parent to the other, and listened. There was no privacy in a one-room cabin. What was said by one was heard by all.

"Well, I don't know's I understand the legal rights all the way," began Tom. "They tell me old man Middleton, who owned all this land in the valley, some ten thousand acres, died and left all the land to his heirs. But before they took possession, through some sort of legal business, years ago, the land had been broke up into parcels and sold. We ain't the only ones. Tuckers and Minguses and LaFollettes, Dyes and Redmonds and Brownfields will all have to get out, too. They're mighty sore, I can tell you, but you can't hit back at the law, not when it's all legal and proper, and they say this is. We may get our money back that we put into it, but it may go like the Sinkin' Spring farm, and we'll not get one cent back. Anyway, I'm pleasured I sold the Mill Creek land when I did; they can't take that away from us, and I've got the money . . . some of it, anyway . . . to put into some land that's safe."

"When do we have to go?" asked Nancy unhappily, thinking of how much she had grown to love this beautiful, fruitful valley. "And where?"

"I hear the Indiana land titles are secure, and you don't have no trouble there like you do here, with titles overlappin' and the first owner comin' out on top, after all. Cousin Hananiah went there, you recollect. He liked it, and so does my brother Josiah, over to Corydon. When I get the crops in, I'll take me a trip over to Indiana and see what I can find out," promised Tom, standing up and stretching, as if he had thrown away all his worry, now that he knew what he was going to do. Meanwhile, it was spring and he was going to get his land all planted, fast, and take from it the biggest and richest crop of everything he could plant before he said good-bye to Kentucky.

On a bright, warm, May Saturday, the seven-acre field, warm and moist and waiting, was ready to be planted. Dennis Hanks, Nancy's cousin, came out from Elizabethtown, where he lived with Aunt Betsey and Uncle Tom Sparrow, and Abe persuaded Billy Mingus to come over and help, too, and they all set out to plant the furrows which Tom ran with a bull-tongue plow. Following Tom and the horse came Dennis, dropping the corn, and after Dennis and Tom came Abe with a big bag of pumpkin seeds. He carefully deposited two fat pumpkin seeds in every other hill and every other row, while Billy came along behind with the hoe and scraped the earth over the seeds so that the crows and blackbirds would not spy them and come down to eat before they had even begun to grow.

It was a beautiful, bright, warm day, the best that early May in Kentucky could offer, which was saying a good deal. New leaves were thin as silk on the trees of the Knobs, and the last of the dogwood splashed its white flowers, like leftover snowdrifts, on the hills. The whippoorwills were back. They sat among the sweet william flowers in the woods and at night flew about, their tremulous calling filling the fragrant evenings.

In the woods near the creek, the tasty, queer-looking sponge mushrooms were at their best, and Miss Emmarilla Dye was out with a tow sack, gathering all she could find. She dried them in strings hung above the fireplace and added them to stews in winter. Tom Lincoln liked sponge mushrooms fresh from the woods, fried in butter or ham grease, but Miss Emmarilla always gave the Lincolns some dried ones anyway, righteously, as if no one could possibly dare to fancy them any other way. Nancy could see Miss

Emmarilla's spare figure up on the hill, bending now and again to pick up a mushroom to add to her tow sack, which must have been getting pretty heavy. Nancy decided to send Abe up to help her with it.

Neighbors in the valley were plowing and planting. The Montos had started their tobacco plants under lengths of muslin to protect them from late frosts, and now the Monto boys and their slaves were out planting the delicate, moss-green plants in careful rows. Horses in the pastures, from one end of the valley to the other, were feeling the good warm sunshine. They frolicked about, kicking their heels. Tom's big red stallion playfully nipped a black mare on the neck, and the mare whinnied so loudly that Tom looked up from plowing and bellowed out:

"You let her alone, you red devil, you!" and laughed. Tom had four good horses that year, the most he had ever owned. Only six other men in the county had as many as that, or any more than he.

It was a big field and a warm day, and in the spring lassitude the boys were tired of their job long before they were finished.

"Gee, Paw, can't we quit now and finish tomorrow?" begged Abe, wiping perspiration in an exaggerated manner from his smooth brow. "It's so hot, we might all keel over with sunstroke. You know what happened to Mr. Hill last summer, don't you?"

Tom grinned. "Yes, I recollect. Mr. Hill was an old man and it was ninety-eight in the shade that day. No fear of a sunstroke for you, boy; you got to keep on and finish today, or I'll tan you good. Tomorrow's the Sabbath and we ain't goin' to do no work, as you rightly know. No, this is the day, and we'll keep on till dark, if need be."

Then, moved by the sight of the boys' hot faces and dejected looks, and the way their pale bare feet, not yet hardened to going barefoot all summer, grubbed into the pleasant, cool, mellow earth, he relented. "I'll tell you what, boys. We'll work till dinner time, and then after dinner, why—we'll all go fishin' for a while. What do you say to that?" The boys whooped. "All right, now, get goin'. You, Dennis, wake up! I declare, you look like you're standin' asleep in the furrow!"

Dennis, who was seventeen and lanky, grinned sheepishly.

The planters moved on, Tom making the furrow, Dennis dropping corn, Abe painstakingly dropping pumpkin seeds and looking for Indian arrowheads at the same time, with Billy Mingus dragging along in the rear with the big hoe, covering up the furrows. Farther on behind, a party of crows, accompanied by several shining blackbirds, paraded in the damp earth, poking about and now and then coming up with a seed. Sally came out and shooed them off several times, but they didn't seem to mind her very much.

Nancy made cornbread and ham gravy at noon, and a mess of wild greens—poke and sour dock and dandelion and wild lettuce—which she had gathered that morning when she went up to talk to Miss Emmarilla on the hill, and she got out the last of the wild strawberry preserves because there was company to dinner. Miss Emmarilla Dye condescended to come down out of the woods to eat, and there were Dennis Hanks, who had an enormous appetite, and Billy Mingus. Nancy brewed up a pot of sassafras tea from the roots Tom had dug in February, and they all drank the bright orange brew, sweetened with maple sugar, because it was good to thin their blood in springtime, Nancy assured them.

Dinner over, Tom and the boys went fishing. Nancy saw the sun begin to slide over the sky, halfway to setting, and still they fished. Now and again a flash of silver would glint in the sunshine, and that meant that there would be perch and sunnies for supper—but would that field ever get planted?

Nancy left her spinning and went out to the creek bank.

"Tom," she warned, "it's gettin' late—it's past three already, and there's a mess of clouds down in the northwest."

Tom looked, genuinely startled. Time for a little while had ceased to be. In the pleasant May afternoon, lazy along the sparkling water, time had not intruded its demands. Suddenly it did, and the afternoon, what there was left of it, fell into its proper niche.

"Get movin', boys!" he ordered, jumping to his feet. "We'll leave the fish on the stringers till supper time. Quick, get goin'! We got to get this field finished before night."

Along about six o'clock, when the sun had slid behind the high-

43

est knob, they were still at it, hard, though Abe and Billy were dragging and cast appealing glances at the house. The crows and blackbirds had quit and gone to roost on the knobs. Nancy waved, and then went to the creek with a big knife and a pan and pulled up the stringers with the fish still alive on them. She proceeded to kill and clean the fish. She laid their shining bodies in the pan and carried them to the house, to be ready to dip in cornmeal and fry in bacon fat when the menfolk were finished.

It was eight o'clock and getting too dark to see when they finally quit. The fish were browning fragrantly in the hot fat, and the coffee smelled wonderful. There was fresh cornbread, and a batch of new butter made that day, and a lot of spring onions which had sprung up from the old winter onions in the garden.

It was cloudy when they went to bed, after seeing that Billy Mingus got home to his own loft bed. Next morning was still gray, but no rain had fallen. The Lincolns, spruce in their best clothes, Nancy in her Sunday bonnet and Tom in his good breeches and coat and silk suspenders, and his best hat, mounted their horses and were off to church. Abe rode with his father, Sally with her mother. Dennis was on his own horse. After services, they went to dinner at Aunt Betsey's in Elizabethtown before coming home in the afternoon to take care of the stock.

It was lowering and gray and thunder rumbled in the distance, far in the north, as the Lincolns rode down Bigg Hill where a wood thrush tuned up in the premature dusk, as if it was night coming on already, though it was only four in the afternoon. The sky was getting mighty dark in the northwest. Lightning slashed through blue-black clouds. Against the darkness, the pale new leaves on the beeches made each tree stand out almost yellow, and the maples turned their fresh leaves inside out in the rising wind.

The Lincolns got home ahead of the storm, but it never reached the valley.

It must have been quite a tempest, though, Tom commented, watching as the lightning chased itself over the sky and thunder banged about. He could see vast gray sheets of rain descending up in the hills at a distance, but except for a little shower which barely wet the dust of the road, no rain fell in Knob Creek valley.

Nancy had just glanced out to see if there was a rainbow, when, startled, she looked quickly again.

She screamed. "Tom! The creek!"

The creek was rising. It was tearing along, bank-full, carrying a load of branches and leaves torn from trees upstream, and, even as the Lincolns watched in horror, it rose above the sheer banks and spread out over the fields. From all the gullies up the arm of the valley where lay Tom's newly planted field, there raced a lake of water, pouring down over the land, while the creek itself, lost in the flood, rose higher still, boiling with mud and debris.

In the space of a few incredible minutes, water was surging past the barn and had almost reached the house, ankle-deep, but it must have been three feet deep out in the field, with the wild current of the creek boiling along with foam and sticks and waves and mud, and a few drowned pullets from up at Gollaher's farm back in the hills.

There was nothing at all that anyone could do. The Lincolns simply stood in the doorway and watched the tremendous run off from the cloudburst as it rushed down the valley and washed out the newly planted field.

"Won't be a seed left in that whole field," mourned Tom. "Not a single seed left!"

"Might as well have fished all day," commented Abe sadly, thinking how his back had ached and how his feet had hurt in the gravel, and how much more fun it would have been to be digging in the cave or fishing along the creek. After that, they all stood and watched in silence.

Night came on and the water was still rushing, but by morning it had gone down. The creek was inside its proper banks again, though still boiling along fast. A layer of mud and debris from the hills lay over Tom's field. He and Abe shucked their moccasins and went out in the squishy mud with a hoe, to where Tom figured there ought to be corn and pumpkin seeds. The two grubbed around considerably and found a few misplaced seeds, but the majority, Tom figured unhappily, had been washed out, long since

45

sent down the creek with Gollaher's dead pullets, and goodness only knew where those seeds would land and maybe one day sprout, to the surprise of whoever owned that land down there. The job would have to be done over.

The way Tom was feeling, that rising tide of discouragement which had been chewing at him for so long, after he had lost the first farm and was being ejected from this one, and now had lost a crop and valuable seed, was getting the better of him. Why did a man tear himself to pieces to work and amount to something when he hadn't a chance, with his fellowmen and the elements all against him?

Mud to their knees, he and Abe plodded back to the house, and in silence scraped the muck from their feet and legs.

That year Abe Lincoln was shooting up like a pokeweed until his pants legs hit him about mid-shin, instead of down where they belonged, and his jacket sleeves came above his wrists, so that he always looked a little like a young rooster done up in feathers that didn't quite fit him. Abe could ask more questions than any child Caleb Hazel had ever known, and it was a challenge to know the right answer, or if not, never to push him off with a half-truth or a lie. Hazel figured he'd be more of a man, and bigger in Abe's eyes, if he up and admitted he didn't know the answers sometimes, and let the boy see that even a man grown, with an education at a college, didn't always have all the answers. The search for truth was the thing, not a man's embarrassment in not knowing: truth was the challenge. He must never let the boy forget that.

He had his chance to impress it upon Abe that spring, when Zachariah Riney, for reasons of his own, suddenly decided to have no more of teaching school in Knob Creek valley, and Caleb Hazel was prevailed upon to take over the job.

In him, the children found a new kind of teacher. Mr. Hazel was exciting. Days with him were full of new things, not only in books but outdoors in the near-by woods and along the stream. Some of the parents complained that their youngsters were sent to school to *sit* in school and learn to read and write and cipher and spell, and that was all. No call to take them traipsin' off into the brush to look for ants and bugs and birds' nests and rocks and all such truck. But the children were so starry-eyed, were so eager to go to school each morning, and the people really did honor Caleb Hazel for his learning, and so they let him teach as he pleased. In most of Kentucky, in most of America, in fact, his way of teaching was new and radical and up for suspicion and questioning, and often for violent censure and dismissal.

It was Abraham Lincoln's good fortune to be among those whom Caleb Hazel taught. The boy was always eager to be out of doors; that was one reason why he enjoyed Caleb's way of teaching, though Tom Lincoln acidly commented that it was just another excuse to get out of work. Abe, said Tom, had a faculty for getting out of work. Like on Saturday when he ought to be home helping with the chores, and he skinned out and wasn't seen for hours.

One splendid autumn Saturday when it was much too fine to waste time in work, Abe went off up the creek, exploring and hunting fossils with Austin and Billy. Austin was oldest, and Billy came between. The trio made a good combination of daring and enterprise, whether it was building a fluttermill in the creek that would really work, or digging a cave, or hunting arrowheads and fossils, or just talking big while the trio lay in the sun and ate ripe papaws.

That day in October the papaws were dead ripe and had fallen heavily on the ground, to lie half hidden among the papery, pale yellow leaves till the hogs or the possums or the boys hunted them out. The fruits were soft and custardy and perfumed, just right to eat with loud slurpings and the seeds spat out.

Abe found a fruit that was pretty soft, too far gone to eat. He held it cautiously in his hand while he rambled about with a studied aimlessness, scuffing up the leaves as if to look for more, and then, when the other two boys weren't looking from where they lay on the ground, Abe skinned quickly up a low tree that hung over where Billy and Austin were reposing, their caps beside them. He leaned over and carefully dropped the overripe papaw into the cap lying next to Austin, directly below.

When he sauntered up, still casually, as if he'd just been rambling around to look for more fruit, he halted suddenly. Austin grinned a gamin grin up at him. The overripe papaw lay splattered messily inside—not Austin's—but in Abe's one and only cap!

Sheepishly, without a word, Abe gathered up his cap and went over to empty out the mess and try to scrub it clean in the creek, pretty thoroughly wetting it inside and out in doing so.

Soon the boys continued on their lazy trip of exploration along the creek, until they spied a persimmon tree full of orange-pink fruit shining in the sunshine across the water. They might not be ripe yet; persimmons usually needed frost to mellow them and take the pucker out, but there was a chance they'd be just right, so the boys sat their way across a fallen tree lying above a deep pool of the creek, inching along with their knees gripping the smooth, barkless log. Austin and Billy got across and Abe was halfway, when the slick wood betrayed him, and he slid around, wildly lost his grip, and fell with a splash into one of the deepest pools of Knob Creek.

He went down and down into the cold, clear water, and bobbed up again, sputtering, then took in a mouthful of creek water that sent him down again. After one awful, paralyzed moment, Austin scooted out on the log bridge and held a stout stick down, so when Abe came up, wild-eyed and taking on more water, he poked the stick down to where the gasping boy could grab it. Abe clutched it with a death grip, and Austin, panting, worked his way along the log, towing his half-drowned friend to where he could touch bottom and wade out.

Abe climbed weakly up on the bank and flopped down. He spat water and gasped gulps of good, fragrant, autumn air and blew and panted until finally he came to enough to sit up.

"Golly!" cried Billy, who had been standing petrified on the bank all this time. "You mighty nigh drowned, Abe!"

Abe nodded, still blowing.

"Austin done saved your life," went on Billy wonderingly, gazing at the hero, who modestly looked at his toe with the rag tied around a stone-bruise. "You'd-a been laid out dead by now, if he hadn't of."

Abe nodded again.

"I—I sure thank you, Aus," he said hoarsely—and promptly coughed up some more creek water. Finally, he got to his feet, water running down his legs and his hair plastered against his head. "Guess I better be startin' home and get on some dry riggin'. Maw ain't goin' to like this when I tell her."

"Don't tell her," blandly suggested Billy. "Lots of things I don't tell my folks, and what they don't know don't hurt 'em—nor my seat, neither! Saves me lots of lickin's."

"She'd know," said Abe hopelessly, looking at his sopping clothes. "I'll tell and get it over with. She don't hardly ever lick me, and Paw's up to court today. Come on, I'm cold."

49

CHAPTER SIX

Tom went about now with a bitter, hard look in his eyes, did a lot of grim staring into space or contemplating the toe of his moccasin while he sat by the fire. The children irritated him. He roared at them if they made a racket, punished them for small misdeeds or for nothing at all, knocked Abe down if he asked a question.

Nancy felt as if she couldn't stand much more of it. Tom had gone on like that for days, for weeks. Sally and Abe were getting to be afraid to come near their own father, and even his dogs shied away when he stomped past them to the barn to care for the horses. But no matter how foul a mood Thomas Lincoln chanced to be in, he never lost his temper with his beloved horses. Out there in the barn, currying their silky hides and lovingly rubbing them down, he eased a little of his tension.

But it all came back again as soon as he was crossed by something in the house.

Abe made the mistake of asking questions again, when he had been warned to keep still—to take his questions, if he simply had to get them answered, over to Caleb Hazel. But Abe Lincoln was only seven, and he forgot, and besides, the question was so important it couldn't possibly wait anyway, and anyway, it was something perhaps only his father could answer.

"Say, Paw," his high-pitched voice spoke up suddenly, out of the long thick silence which lay around his father, who was staring at his moccasin-toe again. "Paw, what's evicted mean? Billy Mingus said his folks and us are bein' evicted pretty soon."

"You shut your mouth, Abe Lincoln!" roared Tom, bringing his chair down to earth with a bang. "I'm fair sick and tired of all your jawin' and yappin' about this and that, when it's no matter of your consarn to find out. March over to that there corner and bring me my stick!"

The tall, thin little boy stood still, frozen, his eyes widening in alarm, his hands behind him.

"March!" ordered Tom, getting to his feet with his heavy face purpling. "Or I'll git it myself and then you'll be sorry!"

"Tom—" began Nancy, frightened, from the door, her hand to her throat.

"Shut up!" thundered Tom at his wife. Nancy and Sally went outside and half ran, both of them silently weeping, to the barn, far enough away so they couldn't hear the sound of the stick whacking down on Abe's back. Sally took her fingers out of her ears, once, to listen.

"I don't hear him yellin', Mammy," she whispered fearfully.

"He wouldn't," said Nancy in a stifled voice. "Abe wouldn't cry out if he was hurt to death!" She buried her face in her hands and the tears trickled through her fingers. The red stallion whickered under his breath and nudged her bent head with his velvet nose.

"Hush, you Red Duke," said Nancy in anger, moving away. "Sometimes I think he loves you better than his own son. His horses never want for anythin', but his young ones—" Nancy again began silently to weep, for she knew not what.

Everything was quiet when Nancy and Sally went back into the house. The little girl looked fearfully about for her brother.

Tom was sitting by the fire, smoking placidly, his face its normal color again.

"Where is he?" asked Nancy in a low voice, not looking at her husband.

"Up in the loft," he said shortly. "Leave him be."

Nancy turned to the fireplace to begin meal preparations, but Sally crept up to the loft anyway, quick and lithe as a squirrel climbing a tree, bare feet avoiding the squeaky rungs of the ladder.

Abe was huddled down in the straw-tick. She burrowed in beside him, kissed his ear, put her arm across his shoulders. She felt him shudder away from her touch and took her arm away hastily, knowing she had inadvertently hurt him where the stick had come down so hard and so often.

"Was it awful, Abe?" she whispered.

He shook his head, mute.

"I never done nothin'," he muttered. "I never done nothin' but ask a question, and I still don't know what it means." He rolled over and sat up suddenly and looked at her with a tear-stained face.

"What *does* evicted mean?"

"It means we're goin' to lose the farm and have to move," answered Sally simply. "You recollect, we heard 'em talkin' about it that night. They've lost the farm. That's why Paw is so mad all the time, and you don't dast ask him anythin' or even speak a civil word to him."

"You mean we got to move away? But we won't be near Mr. Hazel any more, and I won't get to play with Aus and Billy! Golly, where we goin', do you know?"

"Paw said he's goin' over to Indiana to look at some land, seein' as how the land titles is so bad here in Kentucky and he can't keep a farm. I don't know any more than that, though. But I wish we didn't have to move, either. It's fun havin' Mr. Hazel for a teacher. And we never did finish that cave."

Well, that was it. One day in autumn, Tom saddled the Red Duke and fastened on his old saddlebags. He curried and slicked up the stallion until he looked like a show horse ready for the races at Lexington, not as if he was starting on a journey through the wilderness. Nancy put up a big lunch and Tom fastened a small ax and skillet on the saddle and prepared to be gone for a number of days.

"I don't know when I'll be back," he said casually, when he was ready to leave. The Red Duke, with his ears pricked forward, scenting adventure, stamped in impatience to be on his way. In the back of Tom Lincoln's mind there was a queer feeling, as if he had done all this before . . . a memory of a man on a red horse, starting off into the wilderness to find a new home . . . but it was only that half memory of his father leaving Virginia for Kentucky, and of his father before that, leaving Pennsylvania for Virginia, and now another Lincoln was starting off on that same quest.

"If I can find a right good place, I'll corner it and put my option on it and then come back for you," Tom was saying. "You young ones, behave yourselves. Caleb'll come over and do my work, Nan, don't you fret about that. And if you need help any time, you call him. The Monto boys said they'll come and help out, too, if need be."

In a flurry of dust and a thud of hoofs, Tom Lincoln and the Red Duke were off along the Cumberland Trail, toward the winding road climbing Bigg Hill. The maples were flaring scarlet, the beeches gold, when he set off on his quest.

Tom stopped for a drink of buttermilk in Elizabethtown, to wash down the meat and bread he had brought along for his dinner, and he stayed longer than he'd planned because he got into talk with his friends at Crutcher's Store about this and that. The talk ran the gamut of local affairs and got around to politics and what was Andy Jackson going to do with himself, now that he was a national hero, and by that time things were too interesting for Tom to break away.

He leaned comfortably against the wall in Crutcher's, talked and talked—and caught a glimpse of Sarah Bush Johnston as she carried a heavy splint basket of purchases, toting the baby on her hip. The youngster, John D., was whining. Sarah resolutely ignored him and sailed along with sublime disregard of the pestiferous child.

"What that young one needs is a good hidin'," mutter Tom Lincoln to Aram Monto and George Crutcher, watching the progress of Mrs. Johnston and son around the corner of the jail. "Tarnation whinin' brat!"

For Tom Lincoln was remembering his shattering discovery of Sarah a few months earlier.

It was a fine summer day when Tom had come to town to get Nancy some salt and thread and coffee and a length of cambric to make Sally a summer gown. Tom had needed a harness buckle and a new chisel. He was always glad of an excuse to go to town. He had finished his purchases at Crutcher's Store and then went over to Montgomery and Bleakley's, to get a piece of ribbon for Nancy and a pair of silk suspenders for himself and the usual rock candy for the children when, as he was walking past the courthouse, back of which was the jail, he saw a woman he was sure he knew.

She was down on her knees, scrubbing the steps of the jail. A small boy hardly more than a baby played in the dirt close by. Tom had slowed down as he walked, trying to remember where he'd seen that head before, dark hair, curling a little in spite of the cap and the severe way it was pulled back and pinned, when she glanced up from her kneeling position to straighten her back, and their eyes met with a bang.

"For the land of gracious, it's Tommy Lincoln!" said Sarah Bush Johnston, wife of Daniel Johnston, the jailer.

She got to her feet, wiped her soapy hands, red from the scrub water and the harsh lye soap, and put her right hand in Tom's, gave it a brief shake and continued looking at him. Back in her eyes was the memory of the time when the young, callow, silly Tommy Lincoln had actually asked her to marry him—way long ago when he was scarcely grown and she was younger still. Her eyes danced when she remembered how funny he was, with a torn knee in his breeches and his hair standing every whichway on his head. He was considerably improved now, she noted, but it may have been Nancy who had done it. Tom was just a trifle stout, but strong looking and solid, a big man, and his hair did lie down better now, though it was still coarse and black as an Indian's.

"Sally!" Tom was exclaiming, hardly knowing what else to say. Why, I—I—." He was stuck. How could he say that he'd never have thought to see pretty, independent little Sally Bush scrubbing the steps of the county jail?

She seemed to read his mind. Without apology, she said: "Daniel, my husband, is the jailer, as you probably know, Tom.

ABE WAS HALFWAY, WHEN . . . HE SLID AROUND, WILDLY LOST HIS GRIP, AND FELL
WITH A SPLASH INTO ONE OF THE DEEPEST POOLS OF KNOB CREEK.

"WELCOME NEIGHBORS," CALLED THE MAN. . . . "MY WIFE WOULD ADMIRE TO
HAVE YOU ALL COME AND ABIDE THE NIGHT WITH US."

Part of his job is to keep the jail and courthouse clean. Dan isn't well. Sometimes I wonder if he'll last out the year. He coughs so, nights, and his color's bad. It makes him cough more when he works hard, and since we can't afford to pay someone else to do it, I do the cleaning. We keep a clean jail and courtroom, Tommy, in case you'd like to inspect it. I've seen you on jury duty many a time in these past few years. How are your children—and Nancy? I used to see Nancy sometimes, but haven't for a long while."

"They're well," said Tom, preoccupied with his tumbled thoughts. "They're well," he repeated. "Um, I guess I got to get on my way, Sally, but, well—"

"I know, Tom, you're a busy man. Give my love to Nancy and tell her to come in and visit some time."

Standing there on the jail steps, her coarse blue dress somehow startlingly becoming, she waved him off and vanished, with the heavy wooden scrub bucket, into the depths of the Hardin County jail. The little boy, John D., whining, followed her.

That had been months ago. Tom came back to the present.

"Reckon he don't get much bringin' up, now that his paw is so sick," George Crutcher was saying sympathetically, cutting off a piece of cheese and offering it on the knife's point to Tom, who took it absently. "Mis Johnston got all she can do to take care of them two little gals and the baby, keep the jailhouse clean and try to feed and clothe the whole family. I feel right sorry for the woman. Runnin' up bills here in my store, and I ain't got the heart to call them in. Reckon she owes most everyone in town, way things is with her, and it looks like Dan ain't goin' to last much longer. Hard tellin' what she'll do when he's gone to his reward, but I'd trust Sally Johnston to manage somehow. She's a capable woman."

"Used to be a right pretty gal," commented Tom.

Next day, the Red Duke traveled briskly up and down the hills northwest of Elizabethtown and came at last to an eminence overlooking the Ohio River.

It was a fine, broad, shining river, glistening with living fire in the glare of the sunset. Tom Lincoln reined in the Red Duke. Before he sought lodging for the night, he sat for a while on the big stallion and let his eyes take in the winding breadth of the Ohio, looked to where it vanished upstream in the lilac-colored haze and merged downstream with the glitter of the sunset. It was so bright down there it hurt his eyes to look. There was a feather of black smoke in the glow—a steamboat, he supposed, and he would admire to see it, so big and brave, pushing as if by magic against the current of the mighty river. Tom had never seen a steamboat, but the Montos had come home with tales of them, had actually ridden on them, boats which were big and white and beautiful. Their engines rumbled and twin smokestacks billowed smoke. Fine people in elegant clothes, said the Montos, idled in the grand salon or walked about the decks, just riding and having a wonderful time of it, with money to spend and no worries besetting them.

Wistfully, Tom Lincoln watched the steamboat far below him.

"Let's you and me take us a ride on a steamboat, eh, Duke?" he murmured fondly to the horse, rubbing the animal's skull between the pricked ears. The ears twitched back toward the familiar voice, as if trying to understand the words. "We'd get us aboard and ride up the river maybe to Cincinnati, or to Louisville, or somewheres. Maybe even down to New Orleans! We'd have us a time, Duke, that we would!" All of Tom Lincoln's irretrievably lost youth was in his longing.

From far down on the river there came a long, sweet, mournfully mellow whistle, penetrating, possessive, calling to him with an allure which Tom Lincoln could not identify, yet could feel envelop his very being.

He watched the little white steamboat creep slowly upstream into the graying lilac of the dusk, a boat with yellow lights reflecting prettily in the water that looked like some unreal creature from another world. Tom watched it until it had vanished around a bend.

When Tom and the Red Duke crossed the Ohio the next day, they did not ride on a high-style steamboat. They took passage on the ferry which worked its slow way across the massive current of the river and finally landed them on the Indiana shore. Red Duke stepped gingerly down the ramp and took a deep, snuffing breath of the Indiana air, flavored with the scent of the river and of burning wood, as the Indiana settlers, like those over in Kentucky, cleared land and burned the shattered remnants of the old forests. There was so much smoke that it made Tom's eyes sting.

Sixteen miles or so from the Ohio River, Tom Lincoln found a piece of land he liked. It lay near Pigeon Creek, in Spencer County —eighty acres of hilly, wooded land, with a good spring bubbling out of the ground at the foot of a hill. He cornered the land and went to Vincennes to register it, but he paid nothing yet. Craftily, he decided to wait until he had lived for a year on those eighty acres before he put his money into a new farm. The day had passed when Tom Lincoln had plenty of cash money to pay for his land.

Then he set off again for Kentucky. The Red Duke seemed glad to set his slender feet on Kentucky earth again and, with the smell of home in his nostrils, fairly danced down Bigg Hill.

57

CHAPTER SEVEN

Nancy lincoln thought she had never seen such a wilderness as met her eye in Spencer County, Indiana, on the November day when the horses dragged wearily up the last hill. They and the Lincolns had traveled ninety-one miles in five days. Nancy was tired, dreadfully tired, not only from the long ride on horseback, with two children to keep quiet and meals to cook three times a day over a camp fire, but it seemed that inside herself her vitals were tired, weary of moving some place else. She wondered how Tom could do it, and he crowding middle age. A man couldn't go on all his life trying to dig up enough faith and courage to start over somewhere else.

Failure, like a ghost in a graveyard, was leering at them from behind every dark tree trunk in the forest which the narrow road-track bisected, a thin trail of civilization thrust through the wilderness. A chill wind started up and rattled the bare boughs of the oaks with a sound like rushing waters, with a stormy, frightening sound to the four people alone out there with their tired animals, plodding on, on, to the new place where they were to live.

A fox darted suddenly out of the brush and crossed the road, and the Red Duke pranced up on his hind legs, pawing the air, and came down, blowing hard and rolling his eyes. The wind surged through the November trees again, and as far as Nancy's weary, frightened eyes could see, there were the endless ranks of tossing, black, bony boughs against a possum-colored sky.

It was getting late. It seemed that there was no house or habitation for many miles and no place at all to find shelter in the gray and windy wilderness. There would likely be wolves and panthers and bears and no telling what-all, lurking out there in that chill and terrible forest, a forest all tied together with skeins of dried wild pea vines, like some sort of monstrous knitting yarn that had gotten snarled by the wildcat wind and lay tumbled in all directions under the trees. The pea vines were only plants, but they had a sort of deathlike permanence, thin threads so twisted and interwoven with themselves and all the bushes and undergrowth that they would never, never be untangled, and would trap anyone who tried to penetrate them. The pea-vine tangles scared Nancy more than the trees and the darkness coming on. Thank goodness, at least there were no Indians to fear! Panthers and wolves and pea vines were quite enough.

The children were asleep where they rode, Sally in front of Nancy, Abe with Tom on the Red Duke, a pack horse following behind, the brindle cow dragging along at the end of the procession with the hounds. Tom's fourth horse had been sold.

When, at last, Tom rode up into the merest sort of clearing in the forest, on a hilltop, he cried out, "Well, here we are at last!" with a false heartiness which made his voice louder than ordinarily. "Look, you young ones, here's your new home!"

Abe and Sally woke reluctantly, and, hair tumbled and eyes bleary, they stared at the desolate November wilderness.

"I don't see any home," mumbled Abe, ducking down into the warmth of his father's jacket again. "I'm hungry!"

"So'm I, Mammy," said Sally plaintively, with a sound of tears in her voice. "Are we stoppin' here . . . now? With night comin' on, like? I don't see a house . . ."

A wolf, not too far away, set up a mournful and sustained howling, and Sally covered her face with her cloak. Tom jumped down from the Red Duke and soon he was getting out the oats for the horses, was running an experienced hand down the stallion's leg muscles, to make sure he hadn't strained them on the rough roads of the long trip. Nancy and the children stayed in the saddles.

"Well, get down, get down!" Tom cried in impatience. "I'll

start a fire goin', and you get busy on some vittles."

"What's there to eat, Tom?" Nancy asked faintly, climbing stiffly down from her horse and helping Sally. Abe meanwhile had skinned down from the heights of the Red Duke.

"Slice up some of that there pork in the wallet and fry it," Tom said casually. "Get out that cold pone you made yesterday. I reckon it'll soften up if we soak it in hot grease. Hurry up, I'm hungry!"

"You, Abe!" said Nancy firmly, irritation at her husband finding vent to itself in her tone to her son. "Fast! Get busy and find me some kindlin' to start a fire! If you want some vittles to your mouth, you got to help! Where-at is the spring, Tom?"

Tom turned from the Red Duke. "Why, down the hill a ways," he answered, surprised that she didn't know, indicating the direction with a wave of his hand toward the depths of darkness creeping up with the November dusk. "Down there."

Aghast, Nancy looked.

"We'll do without water, then," she said firmly, "unless you go down there yourself, Tom Lincoln, and fetch up some water for us. I won't set foot down there and neither will Sally or Abe till daylight, so's we can see what's waitin' to grab us!"

Tom was momentarily speechless at this defiance.

"There's naught wrong with the location of that spring," he said loudly. "It's right good water."

The wolf howled again, a little nearer this time. The horses snuffled and looked uneasily about. Tom busied himself building a fire, a big, hot fire, too hot to get near to cook by. It lit the surrounding trees, lit the strained faces of the woman and the man and the children, glistened on the hides of the horses, on the mottled hide of the cow. The dogs drew near and flopped down to lick themselves and work on the burs in their tails.

"Well," said Tom conclusively, "seein' as how it's so late, and the horses drank at the last creek we crossed, I guess we'll just do with what we have. I reckon there's still some drinkin' water left in the gourd, ain't there? We'll do with that for tea, and get more in the mornin'. The cow's got to be milked, so the young ones'll

60

have somethin' to drink."

It was late and it was cold and it was frightening. The children were so tired and hungry, they poked and pinched each other, and both broke out crying at once. Tom roared at them. The Red Duke shied at the sound or smell of something unseen in the forest. Nancy, in her nervousness and weariness, upset the teakettle and burned her hand on the skillet.

There came a sudden noise of wagon wheels and horses' hoofs down the road, somewhere in the growing darkness of the Indiana night. The wind blew again and brought the sounds closer, for they came from the northwest. The disheartened people around the fire paused, listening, alarmed in spite of themselves.

A short, heavy man, with black hair showing under his broad-brimmed hat, his strong face accented by deep-set, piercing, dark eyes and a large nose above a thin, sensitive mouth, drove a rattling wagon up to the trail leading in to where Tom Lincoln's fire shot sparks to the sky. The spilled water still sent up steam from the red embers.

"Welcome, neighbors," called the man, picked out in light against the dark. "Name's Josiah Crawford, and I live down the road a piece. My wife would admire to have you all come and abide the night with us. It's a mite cold and like to rain or maybe snow, and you without shelter. We saw your fire, and though we've got naught that's fine nor fancy, we welcome you and would be proud to have your company."

Nancy felt tears pricking her eyes. She stood up, smoothed her hands down her travel-stained linsey-woolsey gown. She tucked a loose strand of hair under her bonnet.

Tom spoke up, as befitted the man of the family. "We're mightily obliged to you, sir. Our name is Lincoln. We've come from Kentucky, a right far piece, and we're a-wearied. We'd be mighty thankful to take shelter with you this night!" He came forward, big, rough hand outstretched.

Josiah Crawford solemnly shook Tom's hand. He looked him over with careful scrutiny.

"Put your young ones in the wagon bed," he directed, "and

61

likely Mrs. Lincoln, too. There's a big buffalo robe to sit on. If she's rid all the way from Kentucky, she'll admire to seat herself on something else but a horse's back. If you'll ride that right handsome stallion of yours, and likely tie the other horses and the cow to the tail of the wagon, we'll get us on our way. Mrs. Crawford will have vittles ready and waitin'.'"

So the Lincolns put out the fire and left the wolf to howl to the grim, dark, wintery sky. Nancy and the children rattled and jounced in Josiah Crawford's wagon, down the stony, hilly road to the level Pigeon Creek bottoms. The small cavalcade splashed through the creek waters, pulled up on the other side and came at last to a house with a porch across the front of it. Light streamed from two windows. Even in her weariness, Nancy could admire them. The Crawfords must be rich—they had glass panes in their windows!

The little, pleasant-faced woman who opened the door took Nancy to her heart.

"Come in and rest you, my dear," said Elizabeth Crawford, putting her hand on Nancy's arm and drawing her into the warm, lighted room. Behind her, a tall young woman smiled a greeting.

"Meet my sister-in-law, Caroline Crawford," introduced Elizabeth, "though we call her Sis, and shall expect you to do it, too!"

"Welcome!" Sis Crawford said cordially.

A fireplace nearly ten feet wide that filled one end of the big room threw out a grateful warmth as heartening as the Crawford kindness. A splendid, exciting smell came to the hungry children.

"What's it I smell?" whispered Abe to Sally. He could feel the salivary juices oozing deliciously into his mouth, had to swallow over and over to keep from drooling at the good odors.

"Must be a burgoo!" Sally whispered back to him. "Oh, won't it taste good, Abe?"

Elizabeth Crawford smiled at the two children.

"Come, come, sit you down. Supper's all ready for the eating!" she cried. She pulled out puncheon benches and chairs and set them along the sides of the big table, filled wooden bowls with the savory stew, placed bowls and spoons and chunks of hot corn bread before the children, before Nancy and Tom, serving the Crawfords last.

"Do you take coffee, friends?" asked Mrs. Crawford politely.

"Yes, thank you kindly, ma'am," answered Tom, and Nancy nodded, smiling gratefully. The coffee was almost better than the stew, and put new life into her weary body.

With the children asleep on a trundle bed, Nancy and Tom sat with the Crawfords and talked of Kentucky. In turn, the Crawfords told them about the Pigeon Creek community, and of the people who were their neighbors.

"You'll find good folk round about to neighbor with you," said Josiah thoughtfully, looking from under his heavy brows at Tom Lincoln and his family. The man was obviously badly off; they'd come with nothing but what they could pack on the horses, yet that red stallion was one of the finest horses he'd ever seen. That stallion represented money and position; a poor man couldn't afford a horse like that. But no one but a poor man could look as hard put as this Lincoln.

". . . . Yes, Miss Nancy, you'll find we've got a fine lot of folk living here," Elizabeth was saying. "Now the Gentrys, they're rich folk, own lots of land and horses and stock. They've got a boy—Allen, they call him—couple of years older than your Abe there. Down this road a piece, beyond our land, you'll find Judge Turnham and his wife and son, David, and the Grigsbys, a big family, and noisy. And there's Brooners nighest to your place, and the Romines and the Hessons and the Oskinses and . . ." She broke off.

Nancy's head was drooping and her eyes kept shutting in spite of herself. "I do ask your pardon," she said in embarrassment, as the kind voice paused and she alerted herself with an effort. "But bein' out in the wind all day, I can't hardly keep my eyes open. . . . I do admire to hear you tell of the folk livin' around here, though. Makes it seem not so much a wilderness as I'd thought. It sounds right friendly-like. I've always hankered to get out of the wilderness, and when we come this afternoon, it seemed like there wasn't a soul in sight anywhere, and it was wilder country than in

Kentucky."

"Yes, there're lots of neighbors," said Elizabeth, her mouth firm, "but you are fair wearied, and I don't aim to keep you up all night with my gibble-gabble. Talk can wait. Josiah," she broke in on her husband's conversation with Tom about the land. "These folk are about done in. Time we bedded them down and got to sleep ourselves. Morning'll be here before we know it.

"You'll take the bed," she said to Tom and Nancy, "and we'll make up pallets on the floor and be asleep in no time."

"Oh, we couldn't take your bed!" protested Nancy. "We'll sleep on the pallets. I wouldn't put you out, you bein' so neighborly, and us such strangers. . . ."

"No such a thing as strangers," said Elizabeth Crawford briskly, getting out quilts from a big chest. "And you'll sleep on that feather tick tonight, or do I have to put you to bed myself? Josiah, you take Mr. Lincoln out to see that his stock is all taken care of proper, while Miss Nancy and Sis and me get ourselves ready for bed. I'll call you when it's all right for you to come in."

Somehow, the friendliness of the neighbors and the warm food and comfort of the Crawford hospitality took some of the bitter edge from the fact that Tom Lincoln was going to have to start all over again to build and clear and plant. Nancy could go the next morning in the sunlight and look over the new place with more understanding eyes, could see why Tom wanted to settle here, although they would be squatters until he made a payment. This land would be his when he made all the rest of the payments, and could not be taken away from him unless he defaulted on them. She wasn't sure how he would make the payments, not in cash, anyway. The days when Tom Lincoln always had plenty of cash money when he needed it seemed to have passed. He had spent most of the money he got from the sale of the Mill Creek farm on the purchase of the Red Duke. Times were tight everywhere, however. Folk traded in produce and skins and labor, but the government always insisted on hard cash. Well, they would worry about that later, Nancy decided, for Tom was cheerful now. The day had turned warm as October and he started at once to cut small trees on the hilltop which he had chosen for the house, working hard.

"I'll just put up a sort of half-faced camp," he explained happily to Nancy. "I'll need help to lay up a real house, and this'll be shelter for us durin' the winter, seein' it's so late."

He put up two forked saplings, high enough for him to stand erect beside them, and bridged the space between with a heavy pole. Then he laid more saplings, as close together as he could place them, from the ridge pole to the ground, and piled the side of the V-shaped shelter with logs. Finally he covered the saplings of the slanting roof with brush to keep out the wind.

"With the roof slantin' down to the ground on the northwest here," he explained, "I'll just leave the front open and we'll build us a big fire there and keep it goin' day and night, and be warm as can be. We'll be like old Dan Boone and John Finley, campin' in the wilderness, won't we, Son?" he joked to Abe, who was not enthusiastic. The boy already missed Austin and Billy, back on Knob Creek, missed going to school to Caleb Hazel, missed the cabin with the loft, so cozy as compared with this chilly, wide-open shelter with leaf-filled ticks thrown down on piles of oak leaves, and no place to cook but at the big open fire.

Nancy, however, finally made a smaller fire to cook by and laid stones in a sort of fireplace to rest the skillet and the kettle on. The big fire was too hot, but they needed that for warmth, so it had to be big.

The winter was hard. Nancy suffered from raw, red, cracked hands and could hardly bear to put them into water day after day, to wash up the noggins and spoons and plates. Meals were monotonous, mostly pork and hominy and corn pone, or squirrel stew. But there were turkeys in the woods and sometimes Tom shot one and she roasted it over the fire until the skin was crackling and brown, and the dogs pranced around in tongue-lolling eagerness to get the leavings. Occasionally Tom brought in a deer, and there was ample table meat for some time, until they all got tired of venison. Then the despised salt pork tasted good again. But, except for wild game, the dwindling supply of ham and fat pork was all they had excepting the daily corn pone. This was cooked in a spider, set three-legged in the coals, with more coals heaped on the iron lid, until the cornmeal cake was baked rock-hard. The cow gave a little milk, but she was due to freshen in the spring, and her milk petered out after a while. With their mush, Nancy gave the children sweetened water. Though this was mighty thin, it had to do. Nancy thought the winter would never, never end. A chance to gather some spring greens, to find wild strawberries fragrant in the grass, to have apples—good, crisp, juicy apples to make into sauce or pies, or just to eat raw—sometimes she thought she could never wait.

She also looked forward with eagerness, but not with a great deal of hope, to the time when Tom would get around to felling enough trees and dressing the logs to make a real cabin with four walls and a loft and a window or two—and a floor that would be easier to keep clean than the dirt floor she'd had at the Sinking Spring farm.

She didn't know why Tom was so shiftless sometimes. He was a good carpenter, and he could work when he was a mind to. It wasn't as if he didn't know anything different. His mother had lived in a nice house on Beech Fork for years, and his folks had come from a fine big brick house over in Virginia which had not only had an elegant oiled floor made of matched boards, but real glass-paned windows and brass doorknobs, and an upstairs and down, and a fireplace in every room. It wasn't as if Tom Lincoln was really white trash, content with a thrown-together camp shack without furniture or floor. He took better care of his horses, of that precious Red Duke, than he seemed to be able to manage for his family. He made very sure that the stock had a barn long before he put up a house. The family still made-do with a half-faced camp that was damp, and wide-open to any varmint which was of a mind to come in. Only the big fire kept the frightening creatures out.

Nancy could sense the prowling pads of wolves out in the darkness, beyond the charmed circle of the fire, as the varmints have been padding and circling ever since man first shut them out by means of the magic power of flame, but waiting, whenever he relaxed his guard and let the fire go out, to step forward and take what they wanted. Nancy saw the wolf tracks, saw the big, blobby panther tracks down by the spring which was so carelessly far from the shelter, a whole quarter of a mile to tote the full bucket, sploshing into her shoes and wetting her skirt, as she struggled uphill.

It was like Tom to have thought of the best location for the house, high and dry and open to plenty of sunlight and away from the bad air of the bottoms, and with an eye to the scenery, too, but without taking thought as to where the water was, nor how far his woman would have to tote it. She hesitated to let the children do the fetching. The forest was still so wild down there, so lone and far from the camp.

CHAPTER EIGHT

"I DON'T WANT you foolin' with that rifle gun of mine," Tom Lincoln warned his son one day. "You ain't old enough to pull a trigger, let alone hit anythin' 'cept maybe the cow or your sister. You let it alone, you hear?"

"Yes, Paw," said Abe, eying the gun. He'd never shot anything, but he always imagined he could. He used make-believe rifle guns made out of long sticks which he picked up out in the woods. He'd hold the pretend-rifle, imagining it with a fine polished stock and a long, cold, powerful barrel—longer than he was tall, almost —and he'd aim at a squirrel, and say:

"Pow! Bang!" and then, "Got him right in the eye!"

Then the squirrel, still lively as ever, would jerk its tail and scold down at him, and Abe would laugh and wave his hand at the little critter.

"Oh, go on with you!" he'd talk back to the squirrel. "I wouldn't kill you if I had me a real gun!" And then he'd make a noise like a squirrel churring and would drive the animal, its tail whipping and lashing in a frenzy, frantic with his teasing.

It really hadn't occurred to Abe to fool around with the real rifle gun until his father told him not to. Then it held a magnetic appeal. It became the thing he most wanted to do. It drew him to it. And when no one was around he would go and feel of its long, smooth, cold metal, would measure with his eye the length of the ramrod and the barrel and discover every time they were just exactly the right length, both of them. He'd slip open the engraved patch pocket to make sure the patches were all there, ready for loading, would heft the powder horn and the neat, heavy lead bullets. Then he'd go over in his mind just exactly how he would load that rifle gun if it was his to do so. He'd imagine how he'd cradle that smooth bird's-eye maple stock, polished as a piece of a lady's fine silk dress, against his cheek, squint just right at a live target, and squeeze the trigger. *Pow!* the game would fall dead with a bullet in the heart—a bear, maybe, or a big buck deer with an eight-prong rack of antlers.

But his paw had warned him not to touch the weapon. Tom Lincoln could whale into him hard enough when he was so of a mind, and Abe didn't relish inviting his wrath any more than he could help. But the rifle fascinated him.

There was a day when his mother had ridden down to neighbor with Mrs. Crawford and Sis, and Sally had gone along. Tom was in town, at Rockport, on business. Abe was left at home to look after the place, and he was to keep up the fire in front of the lean-to.

He was sitting there, toasting himself and teasing the hound-dog, Tobias, who was asleep and jerking his legs every so often, and twitching his nose and whiskers and whining under his breath as if he was dreaming of chasing rabbits. Abe was tickling the pads of the dog's feet ever so lightly to make him twitch a little more. Tobias woke up with a surprised *"Whuff!"* and Abe laughed and rolled over with the dog in his arms.

Then he sat up. There was a sort of low-pitched talking some-where out back!

"Lay still, Tobias," he warned and got to his feet. The sound was coming from the rear of the lean-to. Abe poked a hole in the thatch, applied an eye—and caught his breath. There was a flock of wild turkeys—hens and a big, handsome strutting gobbler—churking and talking and picking about in the tangle of last year's pea vines, to find what was left of the little dried peas. The birds weren't paying a bit of mind to the lean-to, the fire, the boy, or the dog. It looked as if the turkeys didn't know they existed.

The rifle was loaded, Abe knew. Paw always kept it loaded, just in case.

Abe picked it up, and it was heavier than he'd guessed it would be, but nicely balanced. With his fingers he poked the peephole bigger and stuck the end of the long, smooth bore of the Kentucky rifle through it. He put his eye to the sight, drew a bead on the nearest turkey gobbler, squeezed the trigger and then fell over backward as the gun kicked and laid him out flat.

When his head cleared and he got to his feet, with shaking hands he laid the gun back in its old position in the corner, and only then did he look out at the turkeys. They'd all scattered, gabbling frantically, flying and running off into the pea vines of the forest. But there was a big heap of bronzy feathers lying fluffed at the edge of the clearing. Abe ran out, the dog with him, snuffing at the dead gobbler.

Abe picked up the bird gingerly and, still feeling a little dazed, carried it back to the lean-to and laid it in the corner with the rifle. Paw would likely whale the daylights out of him for using the gun, but at least he'd provided table meat for the family.

Abe felt a little sick. He figured he liked the looks of the handsome turkeys, strutting about, all unafraid, among the tangles of pea vines and under the beeches, hunting nuts, more than he relished the look of the heap of dead feathers with the bloody, torn, wobbly head which was the turkey he'd shot. He was feeling sicker. He didn't like the notion of killing things, even vittles to eat. He liked well enough to eat 'em, but it was another thing to do the killing himself. He'd likely starve to death if he had to go out and hunt his own meat, he figured. He got up hastily, then, and went out back of the lean-to and lost his breakfast. When he came back, he felt shaky but a little better, but he still didn't relish the thought of what he'd done.

When Tom arrived home, Abe told him about it. Might as well get it over with.

"Paw," he confessed, "I used your rifle gun today."

"You did what?" roared Tom. "Abe Lincoln, you got no call to disobey me! I told you and I told you not to touch that there gun of mine, and now you up and do it and then brazen it out. What—"

"I shot a turkey with it, Paw," said Abe in a low voice, looking down at his moccasin where one big toe was poking through.

"You shot—what?" cried his father.

"I shot a turkey. With one shot, right in the head. I wish I hadn't of, Paw. He looked so pretty walkin' about, and then he was just layin' there dead. I reckon I ain't goin' to shoot anything else as long as I live!"

"Why, boy," cried Tom, going over to look at the big turkey, forgiveness in his heart, suddenly, "you're a right good shot! And although you got no right to use my gun when I tell you not to, anyways, I'm proud of you! That turkey'll taste mighty good tonight, and I reckon maybe your maw'll make us some turkey stew with flat dumplin's tomorrow! I won't lick you this time, boy! But don't you dast use that rifle gun again till I tell you!"

"No, Paw, I sure won't!" promised Abraham Lincoln fervently.

As spring moved into Indiana, great flocks of passenger pigeons came through. Some stopped in the trees along the creek and broke down boughs with the sheer weight of the birds. The wild turkeys were walking furtively, going the roundabout way to the nests they were hiding under wild gooseberry bushes in the woods. Foxes and possums were nosing around, hunting for turkey eggs or for the delicate, speckled young. A phoebe nested under a ledge of the barn, and a wood thrush caroled at sundown in an oak near the Lincoln lean-to. Nancy, looking up from stirring the hominy, listened to the infinitely beautiful tones of the cinnamon-brown bird whose spotted ivory breast the late sunlight lit with a radiance that caught the new velvety oak leaves, too, in its illumination.

Spring—spring at last! And with the sunshine warming more every day and the restlessness of springtime upon everyone, the whole interior of the lean-to shack seemed somehow outgrown, a shell to be shed away. Nancy hoped that Tom would start building the new house soon. He'd have to get the fields planted first though; she knew that. And in order to have fields, there'd have to be a log-rolling to get the felled trees out of the way. With Abe's sturdy help with an ax on the smaller stuff, Tom had spent the winter cutting down these trees. Abe was so big and strong now, at eight years, that he was a big help to his father, once Tom got him working. It was often difficult, however, to get Abe's attention away from watching the wild things around him and studying out the whys and wherefores of insects and plants and animals.

"I've been and passed the word around that we're to have a log-rollin', come Saturday," Tom announced one March day when the frogs in the bottoms were singing away like mad, and woodcocks were walking solemnly about down there where the creek had overflowed and gone back again, leaving thick black mud.

"If we can git one field cleared, I'll be satisfied. I can plant beans and flax and suchlike between the fallen butts over in the east field, but I got to have open ground for proper corn. Josiah Crawford says we'll have plenty of help at the rollin', so it's up to us to see that we got vittles for 'em. Mis Crawford'll help out, and I hear tell Mis Brooner'll bring over a ham, and Sis Crawford, she says she'll bring a deep-dish apple pie. You might make some of them good flat dumplin's in turkey gravy. I'll go out and get me a gobbler. They're still a-plenty of them around, but deer are too puny and poor this time of year to bother with. With ample bread and drink, we'll have a bounty of vittles, and worth it to have help with that there rollin'."

The log-rolling was downright heady excitement. Abe had never seen an affair like it before. After a winter of loneliness in the woods, it was exhilarating to watch people gathering, to hear talk and laughter and see faces other than those of his own family.

Josiah Crawford drove up in his wagon with Mrs. Crawford and Sis, with the deep-dish, dried-apple pie and a pan of beans baked with pork. The Crawfords busily set about laying rough planks on stumps to make long tables and covered them with long strips of linen Mrs. Crawford had brought along. The linen transformed the planks and stumps into dignified tables, waiting for the food and the pleasures of neighborly hospitality.

Mrs. Brooner walked across the field with her son, Allen, toting the baked ham. Mrs. Turnham rode up sidesaddle. She carried a basket containing flannel cakes and a crock of pickles. Other neighbors brought contributions. It was the most food Abe Lincoln had ever seen in his life, all laid out at once.

Forest trees which had been growing there for so many years, some for centuries—beech and red maple and sugar maple and white oak and sassafras and sweet gum and walnut—were lying stretched on the ground where Tom Lincoln's ax had laid them.

Now, with their spike poles and other poles without spikes, the men were ready to begin heaving and pushing, getting the fallen trees to moving.

The workers were divided into two competing teams.

"One, two, three—heave!" shouted Bill Barker, a tall, lean, young giant with a mop of pale yellow hair that blew in the March wind and shone like young corn silk. "Once more, one, two, three, *heave!*"

A big black walnut, three feet in diameter, turned over, and from under it a family of bobwhites scurried out in fright, dashing away and piping to the shelter of a distant brush pile. The log went over, again and again, until it came to the big burning place. In a separate spot, Tom Lincoln had piled the logs which would some day become his new house—when he had time to get around to building it.

On the other side of the cluttered field, which looked as if a giant had been playing jackstraws and had dropped trees like straws every whichway, James Grigsby was leading his own team. Families gathered on the side lines and cheered their men. And the logs rolled—the big, smooth-barked, gray beeches and the rough-barked maples and oaks, and the smaller stuff, and the green boughs of the sassafras, fragrant when bruised by the pushing poles. The boys gathered for their own log-rolling among the smaller trees and made more noise at it than the men.

"Go it, Bill!" cried Alf Myler.

"Heave into it, Jim!" cried someone else. "They're goin' to win if you don't take care!"

Slowly, yet with remarkable speed considering the size of the

73

great logs being rolled by sheer man power across Tom Lincoln's new field, the space was being cleared. The log piles grew into massive pyres.

"Done!" cried Josiah Crawford. "I declare it a tie. Done to the minute! Let's give 'em a cheer!" And the men whooped and yelled and threw their hats into the air.

"Bring a light, bring a light!" they yelled. The sun was setting when the first yellow flames, brought in a gourd from the big fire by the lean-to, were set to the dry stuff between the logs. While night came down and the log-rollers were busy eating, the flames rose higher and higher, roaring now, throwing sparks to a sky whose spring stars were dimmed in the great conflagration. The twin fires seemed to compete with each other in sending soaring flames upward, licking into the brush and chewing into the great solid trunks of trees which burned with a deep, steady, dedicated flame. In Tom Lincoln's east field, the primeval trees of Indiana were going up in red sparks and white smoke, burning intensely with blue flames and great heat, the smoke fragrant. These would die down finally, while the merrymaking went on, but the coals would last until the next day.

Esau Wagner, the fiddler from Rockport, sawed away and the dancing began. The men had labored like giants in rolling the tons of logs to the burning, but the food laid out on the strips of linen over rough planks had reinforced them, and they stamped out the figures until ten. By then the light of the great fires was dimming, and the March wind blew cold and damp. With the dying down of heat and light, so did the enthusiasm wane.

"Gather up your truck and come away; time we went home," said Peter Brooner, yawning, to his wife. Josiah said the same to Elizabeth, and one by one the families went off.

Sis Crawford, standing tall and handsome in her sprigged, black bombazine gown, watched while Bill Barker, taller even than she, took another dipperful of cider. She turned on her heel.

"Wait, I'll go home with you," she said briefly to Josiah and Elizabeth Crawford.

"I thought Bill Barker was goin' to carry you home," said

Josiah, scowling at his sister and casting a suspicious eye over to where Bill was doubling up in laughing at a joke.

"Bill's had too much cider tonight!" snapped Sis, tossing her head. "I'd not trust him to get any rig across Pigeon Creek in the dark, in the state he's likely to be in. Say no more about it, Brother. Take me home!"

Bill Barker saw the team moving off, caught a glimpse of Sis Crawford's erect head in the crisp bonnet.

"Wait, Jo Crawford!" he yelled, sprinting on his long legs toward the wagon. Josiah turned his head somewhat grimly. He felt as if he were set between two strong forces, in a position to be smashed when those forces clashed.

"Whip up the horses!" ordered Sis Crawford. "I don't want to have words with the sot!"

But Bill was there. "Look, Sis, you promised I should carry you home from the log-rollin'. How come you're startin' off like this?"

"I promised a sober man, not one filled to the ears with hard cider, so's he can hardly stand straight!" cried Sis Crawford, her big, black expressive eyes all but snapping sparks into his surprisingly innocent-looking, bluebell-colored eyes under pale, silky brows.

"I ain't!" he cried in defense. "Look! I can stand straight and I can walk straight, and I'm goin' to carry you home like I planned. Cider doesn't hurt a man, and I don't touch spirits. You know that, too, Sis Crawford. Get down, or I'll heft you out of that rig myself!"

Sis Crawford held tight. Her black eyes bored holes in him.

"Here I sit and here I stay till I get home. Go along, Brother."

Josiah, out of patience with both of them, frowned over his massive nose, whipped up the team and drove at a spanking pace down the road. Bill Barker stood where he was, saying things under his breath until Sis was out of earshot. Then he let fly with remarks that peppered the air. Nancy, not far away, looked up.

"I beg your pardon, Miss Nancy," he muttered and joined the other young fellows over by the heat of the dying fires.

75

There came a day when, after a soft April rain, the damp brown field was marked with long rows of little green feathers of the sprouting corn, and with the tufts of pumpkin leaves. Tom planted flax and beans and cabbage and onions among the fallen trees in the uncleared field, and Nancy and the children scratched about with the hoe to get out weeds and wild flowers. It was hard to kill out the woodland plants which for so many generations had sprung up there. Into the glare of sunlight came wild geraniums, putting out pink flowers which paled in the more intense light of open sunshine. Colonies of May apples opened up, like a host of elves holding umbrellas, and it was a job to hack them off. The cows wouldn't touch them nor would the horses. Folk said May apple leaves were poison, and Nancy was afraid even to have the children playing around them. The umbrellas were better off wilting in the hot sun.

Spring moved warmly into summer and burned down on the hills, drying out the earth which was exposed. Heavy rains had washed some of the rich topsoil of Tom's new fields down the slope and into the bottoms, and the fields dried out quicker than the woods did with their cover of leafmold. It was a hot, dry summer, and Nancy's flax didn't do very well.

"I'll have to wait and gather nettles; I see there's a power of them down in the bottoms. Aunt Betsey used to say you could make a rough sort of linen out of nettles, most as good as you could of flax. We got to have something to make garments out of for next year, flax or nettles. I do wish we could have sheep, Tom, so's we could have some wool. Don't you figure we might, by next year, maybe?"

"We can't have no sheep until we get shut of them wolves!" snapped Tom, irritable in the heat. "They prowl around and carry off every blasted lamb that's born about here, and harry the ewes till they fall over—and then cut their throats, quicker than you can think. I never saw such varmints! A man can't hardly keep any stock 'cept'n things bigger'n wolves and panthers. I want to have me some hogs and chickens and geese, soon's we get some of the varmints cleared out—or else build pens that'll keep 'em out. Till then, don't complain to me about it; it's none of my doin'!"

"It was your idea to come to Indiana," remarked Nancy acidly. "I never asked to break away from Kentucky to come here where it's wilder than it was back there!"

"I know it was my idea!" thundered Tom, his face darkened in rage. "And you have no call to throw it up to my face every whipstitch. It's a good country and they can't take my land away from me over here in Indiana, and I aim to stay here till I die!"

"I guess likely," said Nancy bitterly, pushing the damp hair away from her perspiring neck. "You got the money for your first payment yet? The whole of the eighty dollars is got to be paid by the end of the year."

"No, I ain't got it yet, and you know I ain't, and I'll thank you not to keep on a-askin' if I have. I'll git it in good time. Now shut up!"

With the summer as hot as it was, it was just as well to keep on living in the wide-open lean-to, figured Tom, who also felt it was too hot to work. At least the half-faced camp was cool at night, though the south sun bore down hard all day, until Tom put up a sort of porch-shelter made of poles and a frame overlaid with cattails and rushes from down in the swamp near the creek.

It was late summer when a pair of horses, bony nags straining at the seams, plodded up the dusty road of the Lincoln hill above Little Pigeon Creek. The woman in the sidesaddle of the one horse looked as knotty and lean as the steed itself, and the man was not much better, seedy and whiskered.

"Land, Thomas, if this ain't the place, I shall jest die, I know I shall!" said the woman, wiping her face. "We should-a sent them word so's they could-a been on the lookout for us or at least come to meet us. They ain't a sight nor sound of anyone around," she complained nasally, "jest like on that other hill where we done stopped. Maybe we been directed wrong. I tell you, Thomas, I'm about wore out!"

"I'm certain sure this is it, Betsey," soothed the old man, reining in his horse, though it had stopped of its own volition after the climb up the hill and stood blowing and heaving, as if it had climbed a mountain. "If that ain't Tom Lincoln's black-and-tan hound, name of Tobias, then my name ain't Tom Sparrow! Yeuh! Yeuh! Tobias! Here, Tobias!"

The hound looked up from where he was scratching fleas in the shade of a sassafras tree, flopped his tail amiably and got up slowly.

"That's him a-right," said Tom Sparrow in satisfaction, "but land only knows where the rest of the family is at. Hey, Tom! Tom Lincoln, where be ye! *Hallo-o-o-o!*"

"I do wish Denny'd come along with us, 'stead of stoppin' off back there at that tavern. Likely he'll drink too much and he won't be no good for nothin' till tomorrow. And if Nancy and Tom ain't to home, I'd like to know where we'll lay our heads this night! It's a forsaken wilderness, that's what it is!"

"Denny'll be along; said he'd catch up with us. Never fear, he'll be here for supper! Never knowed Dennis Hanks to miss a meal. Hey, there's little Abe! Looks like he's growed a foot. Hey, Abe, where's your Mammy and Pappy?"

Abe Lincoln stopped in his tracks and stared. He didn't recognize the thin, old, whiskery man sitting humped on the bony horse . . . and then it dawned. It was Uncle Thomas Sparrow— and it must be Aunt Betsey with him. His mother would feel good now. She'd been fair pining away for a sight of Aunt Betsey, who was like a mother to her, and Uncle Tom, who was like a father. Abe started on a run to greet the newcomers.

"Howdy, Aunt Betsey. Howdy, Uncle Tom. Why don't you git down? You goin' to stay? Maw's down to Crawfords with Sally, and Paw's out in the back field. I'll call him!" He turned and raced off, bellowing, "Paw! Paw! Come see who's here!" Before long, he came dashing back to the visitors.

Tom Sparrow climbed creakily down from his horse, which took a deep sigh of relief to be rid of its burden, though Tom was so light in weight that he looked as if he would blow away in a high wind. Betsey, too, was as spare as a craney-crow in a burned-

78

over swamp.

Tom Sparrow helped Betsey down. She exclaimed in bitterness at the stiffness in her joints. Tom Lincoln came on a lope, hand outstretched in welcome.

"Why didn't you let us know you was a-comin'?" he cried. "Nan's been fair pindlin' and pinin' for a sight of you. Looked like I'd have to go get you or else take her back for a visit, she's been so lonesome-like. You come for a long visit?"

"Yes, Tom," spoke up Betsey. She'd never liked Tom much, mainly because he'd up and married her Nancy and had taken her away from the Sparrow household where she'd spent so much of her life like a beloved daughter. Betsey had thought for a while, though, that Nancy had bettered herself, seeing as how Tom Lincoln had money and owned land and horses in Kentucky. But it looked to her now as if maybe she'd been right in the first place, and he wasn't good enough for her Nancy nor ever would be. Certain-sure, looking quickly around with an all-encompassing and critical eye which took in everything, she saw that Tom had not exactly built his family a mansion, nor even a whole house. If that little lean-to with the weeds on the roof was what the Lincolns lived in, then land only knew where their kinfolk would lay their heads.

"Where you livin' at now, Tom?" she asked cautiously, forming her words with her thin, dry lips, as if they pained her to utter them, knowing as she did the probable answer. She sucked her snaggy teeth, waiting.

"Right here, Aunt Betsey," said Tom cheerfully, waving a big hand proudly in the general direction of a small clearing with the lean-to in the middle of it. "Abe, you go run down to Crawfords and tell your Maw and Sally to get up here and see who's come to visit. How long did you say you was fixin' to stay?"

"We're aimin' to live with you," said Betsey Sparrow sourly, eyeing the lean-to, "but I don't rightly know where-at you'll bed us down, Tom Lincoln; I don't, for a fact. I'm surprised you don't have a better house built by this time. You mean to say you lived in that there shack all last winter?"

"Sure we did, and liked it," said Tom stoutly. Aunt Betsey always riled him, though he tried to be polite to the old girl, just because she meant so much to Nan.

"We brought along what we needed," said Tom Sparrow. "Just our feather tick and Betsey's best riggin' and the Bible—and not much else. Toted everythin' and us on the two horses, so there wasn't much room, but it'll do us. Likely we can buy or trade for what else we might need. You got stores here? I let out my farm in Kentucky. The rent money'll come in handy."

"Yes, we got a store over to Jonesboro," said Tom, "and lots of 'em down to Rockport. Well," he went on, rumpling his hair, "I'm sure glad you brought beddin', because we ain't got much right now. Nancy'll be up soon from the neighbors, and she'll get you settled. What'd you do with Dennis? He stay in Kentucky?" he asked hopefully. Dennis Hanks always set wrong with Tom and irritated him more than somewhat. It would be a matter of thanksgiving if Dennis had stayed in Kentucky. But Tom's hopes were immediately dashed.

"Denny's done stopped at the tavern over to Jonesboro," said Betsey grudgingly. "I reckon he'll come up here when he's a mind to. I'd admire to have a cup of tea or whatever. I feel a mite faint, Tom Lincoln."

Nancy rode up in a hurry with Sally, and her tearful joy at sight of Betsey and Tom Sparrow compensated for Tom Lincoln's aggravation at having kinfolk on his hands. Supper was about ready when there came a racket on the road, the noise of a gun going off at intervals, and a loud and enthusiastic whooping.

Dennis Hanks was approaching.

Dennis was an overgrown boy the size of a man. Although he was only eighteen, he looked and acted like a man grown. He had a stubble of beard that would have been the better for having had the attentions of a razor, and language fit to take the hide off a panther. His broad-brimmed hat was squashed down firmly over his unkempt and ragged long hair. He was clapping his heels hard into his horse's ribs, and the horse, snorting and blowing through inflamed nostrils from the ride up the hill, was still being belabored when Dennis rode with a yell and a flourish into the clearing.

"Hi-ho! Here I am!" he bugled. "Howdy, Nancy! Howdy, Tom— Hey there, is that Abe? And looks like Sally's about a young lady grown, big enough to take out sparkin'! Whooop! Hi!" He had reloaded his pistol by now and he fired it off again, while the frightened horse reared, and the hound-dog yelped and cut out into the timber. Tom Lincoln, roaring mad, leaped to the horse's bridle and brought the animal down to earth.

"Get off that there horse, Dennis Hanks!" he ordered. "Afore I have to knock you off! You crazy or somethin'? Actin' like that when you come visitin' your kin! Treatin' a horse like that— kickin' a hole in its ribs, likely, with them heels of yours, and deafenin' the poor critter and us with all that fool shoutin' and shootin'! Git down, I say, or I'll take you off in a way you won't like. Git!"

Dennis, grinning, slid off the horse. He knew Tom Lincoln was as strong as three men and he could do as he said, big as Dennis was. He stood there, grinning foolishly, wavering a bit in his tracks.

"Go lay down," ordered Tom grimly. "You look's if you need it. Sleep it off. Or if you kin set up and eat like a human bein', come join us; supper's on."

Tom looked at Nancy and Betsey, who were watching silently, and at old Tom Sparrow, who was grinning almost as foolishly as Dennis, but for a different reason. Tom Sparrow never could manage this foundling, this waif of a relative of Betsey's, her own sister's boy, left in their care. Dennis was wild. Meek little Tom Sparrow had long since lost any control he might have had over the gawky, overgrown boy who had so quickly developed into a wild and wayward man, yet still had a boy's ungoverned love of crude fun. Dennis slumped down on Betsey's feather tick, spread over the leaf bed, and very quickly and conclusively was asleep.

The family ate in silence. That night the Lincolns made room in the lean-to, somehow, to accommodate three more people. And it was this advent of kinfolk—with Uncle Tom's hacking and coughing all night long and Aunt Betsey's tobacco pipe and complaining during the day—which, perhaps, urged Tom Lincoln into starting work the very next day on the new house which he had put off building.

The neighbors came over for the house raising. Dennis's strength came in handy, when he could be persuaded to use it. Tom Sparrow, for all his years, helped a little, too, and Abe exerted muscles which proved that, even at the age of eight, he, too, had the Lincoln strength.

The logs rose in a rectangle in the usual pioneer pattern of 18 x 20 feet, and Nancy's heart rejoiced that she would have a real house again. Tom was thankful that he built when he did, because, within a few weeks after the Sparrows came to Indiana, more kinfolk followed—Lucy Hanks Hall and her husband, Levi, and their sons, William and Squire—but they declined to camp long with the Lincolns, and built a cabin close by on Tom's land.

CHAPTER NINE

A YEAR PASSED, and the summer of 1818, like the summer before, was terribly hot and dry. The flax crop failed again, and Nancy, Aunt Betsey, stout Lucy Hall and the barefoot children all went down into the dry, weedy bottoms, where the earth was cracked and hard and the creek low and stagnant in the drouth, to gather nettle stalks. They brought armloads of them down to the spring, an area which was still muddy, and buried them just beneath the surface. The water in the mud, warmed from the late summer heat, would rot the nettle stalks so that only the fibers would remain. It was prickly, uncomfortable business. The workers had to be careful to protect their arms from the terrible nettle prickers. Abe was always forgetting, though, and brushing against them. Then he would have to shuck his clothes in a hurry and dive into the swimming hole—a good excuse, Aunt Betsey always said, sourly—to get away from the fire in the nettle stings. When the nettles were rotted, they were taken out of the mud and the fibers were washed and beaten. In September, Nancy managed to spin them into a coarse, linenlike thread on her little flax wheel.

It was still hot weather, and dry, and most of the green things had perished in the heat, though in the woods there still were green plants—snakeroot and joe-pye and asters and sticktights, burgeoning lush and green. Although the cow usually kept away from snakeroot plants, she ate the big juicy green leaves eagerly now in the dry weather, for want of anything better, and the

83

poison in the leaves made her grow visibly thinner. She would stand all day, shaking and sick-looking. Her calf had hardly strength enough to suck and would fall down, pitifully moaning, and lie there shaking, too.

Tom was worried. He'd heard of how the cows got sick at this time of year, and how human-folk took down, too, with the same ailment. There was a growing lot of sickness in the neighborhood, in addition to the usual chills and fever which afflicted folk, especially in the bottoms where the mosquitoes were so bad. Now something was attacking children and adults alike. They'd get a terrible feeling of weakness and a burning in their vitals, and their tongues turned brown. Their eyes were queer-looking, and for want of strength the sick people took to their beds.

The fever usually ran for ten days. If folk survived these ten days, they usually got well. But in the summer and autumn of 1818 many a one did not. The burying grounds, the little family plots back in the woods or on the hills, had new graves hacked in the baked, hard earth.

Nancy Lincoln visited the sick as often as she was able to. She brought soup to them and tried to help all she could. There was so little anyone might do, though Nancy and Elizabeth Crawford often rode together to the homes where sickness was, and Nancy often came home late, exhausted, and would weep to think of another soul departed the earth. She worried about Abe and Sally, especially when Sally looked peaked and lay for three days burning with a fever and could eat nothing because she muttered that her tongue felt too big. But she grew better, and soon was up again, though thin and pale.

Thomas Sparrow looked drawn and gaunter than ever. He seemed to feel the hand of death in the Indiana wilderness, and he prayed often and stared unseeing into the dry woods where weeds standing high were parched and drooping and dusty for want of rain.

One day Thomas Sparrow could not rise from his bed. His fever was high. His tongue turned brown. Nancy tended him, while Betsey wrung her hands and paced. On the sixth day after he was taken down, Thomas Sparrow died of the milksick. Betsey collapsed. Four days later she, too, was dead.

Tom Lincoln and Dennis whipsawed planks to make the coffins, and during the burning days of late September, when there had still been no rain, they gouged two graves in the earth on the hill south of the cabin, there where the deer trail headed toward Pigeon Creek and the valley. Dennis and Tom worked on Thomas Sparrow's grave until the perspiration stung their eyes. Flies and mosquitoes tormented them. At last the graves seemed deep enough, and there was the burying. Josiah Crawford rode over to help, and young Allen Brooner came and stood with Abe, wide-eyed and wondering, to watch.

"My maw ain't feelin' so pert," commented Allen to no one in particular, but there was fear in his voice. "You think likely she'll die, too?" Abe nudged him to be still.

Nancy went to see Mrs. Brooner after the burying of Aunt Betsey. She could not bear to go back home and think. It was better to be doing something for someone else, and poor Mrs. Brooner was very ill. Nancy's eyes were dry and hot with unshed tears. Part of herself, all her childhood memories of love and kindness which the Sparrows had given her as if she were their own beloved child, lay buried in the brown earth of the graves beside the deer trail. . . . Mrs. Brooner, massive on her bed which had come all the way from Maryland in a covered wagon, stared bleakly into space, muttered for water and burned with fever.

When Nancy went home, she felt weak in the knees. She tried to tell herself that it was all on account of her grief for her kin, and because of the heat and walking all the way home from Brooners.

She felt no better by morning. She had a fever, and her tongue felt queer. The children hung around, watching her, a nameless fear thudding in their pulses—watching their mother who had always been the strength of the household, knowing what had happened to Aunt Betsey and Uncle Tom and to Mrs. Abels and her baby, and those others of whom folk spoke in hushed tones, dead of the milksick.

"Don't you dast to drink any more milk, Abe," whispered Sally fiercely. "Not even if there was naught else to eat or drink, nothin' to put on your mush or—or—just don't you dast to take a sip. That's what's killin' folk. You see how the cows is actin', queer-like, and so many dyin' of the trembles. They've eaten somethin' that's poisoned them, and it's poisonin' us, too. Mammy's been poisoned like Mis Brooner and Aunt Betsey and the others. You note how good Paw's doin', and he don't touch milk because he says he hates the taste. And there's Dennis, too, he don't touch it, and look how healthy he is. Now, you recollect, Abe, and quit drinkin' it!"

On the eighth day, Nancy Lincoln closed her weary, hot eyes and never opened them again. It was October 5, 1818, and a storm, loud with thunder, wild with wind, cooling with blessed rain, came and cleared the air, freshened it deliciously to skins which had been hot and perspiring for so many days and nights; but it came too late to comfort Nancy. The rain damped down the dust and made it easier for Dennis and Tom and Josiah Crawford to dig still another grave next to Mrs. Brooner's, up on the hill beside the deer trail.

"Abe, you git busy and make pegs to hold these here planks together," said Tom tightly, his whole body weary from the closeness of death all around him, weary with his desperate inability to fend it away from his loved ones. It seemed to him he had smelled the very presence of death in the hot dry air which was now so mercifully cleared by the rain.

Maybe the rain was the end of the sickness . . . but in its going, Tom had lost his wife. In some ways, while digging the grave, he could not believe it was really she who lay in the newly made coffin of whipsawed wild cherry planks which only so lately had been a living tree in the forest. It was not Nancy. She was only away, visiting one of the sick, calling on Elizabeth Crawford, helping Sis Crawford with her linen bleaching, making do with the best she could glean from the woods to build their lives here on the Indiana hill.

It was not Nancy—it couldn't be. He hadn't finished her house

WITH REMARKABLE SPEED CONSIDERING THE SIZE OF THE GREAT LOGS BEING
ROLLED . . . ACROSS TOM LINCOLN'S NEW FIELD, THE SPACE WAS BEING CLEARED.

"WELL, WHAT'RE YOU WAITIN' FOR?" SNAPPED TOM, IMPATIENT IN HIS NERVOUS-
NESS. "CAN'T YOU SAY HOWDY TO YOUR NEW MAMMY?"

yet. He'd promised her a floor, a smooth wood floor, but he hadn't got around to it yet, and it was still only an earth floor. He'd promised windows with glass panes, but he never had had the money. It had been all he could do to scrape together the eighty dollars for his land payment. There had been nothing left for glass for the windows, so they were covered with greased paper, which let in some light but you couldn't look through them as you could at the Crawfords'. Nancy had wanted furniture, too, but Tom hadn't had time to make the nice corner cupboard for the dishes she'd hoped to have some day, nor the splint-bottomed chairs, only three-legged stools. No proper bed, just a pole bed made of withy poles supported part way by a corner of the room. She'd longed for so many nice things that women like, so many of the good, comfortable, fine things a body had every right to want, to make living easier and prettier, and he'd only managed to get the shell of a house together before she'd left him. He was forty years old, and here he was in no better house than he'd had when he was first married, or even poorer—and now he had no wife, only the two children, and the Lord only knew how he was to care for them. He wept silently, not so much for what he had lost, but for the things that had never been, and that now would never be.

They buried Nancy. And the deer that night paused, light-footed and wary, and sniffed at the heap of damp, newly turned clay which had never before seen the light of day nor the glint of moonlight. The deer left their pricked tracks in a corner of it and leaped on, white-tailed and flighty, along their trail which was moist and sweet-smelling after the glorious rain. The sounds of migrating birds went over in the night, and a nine-year-old boy lay wide-eyed and awake in the loft of the unfinished cabin on an Indiana hilltop, and wondered about his mother.

He wondered if she was still there in her coffin with the pegs in it he'd made himself, or if she was in heaven, as she always said happened to folks when they'd lived a good life. His mother had been good, he knew. He wasn't so sure about himself, sometimes, or about Dennis, or even about his father, but he was sure about his mother. If she was in heaven, then she was all right, and likely happy to be with Aunt Betsey again, but if she wasn't . . . some tears squeezed out of his eyes in the darkness and he let them run. It eased some of the hurt inside him. He let them run until his nose was snuffy and he couldn't breathe so well. Then he stopped crying and pretty soon he was asleep.

Moonlight lay silvered over the autumn woods and on the roof of the cabin. It was very quiet out on the hill.

CHAPTER TEN

It was a long, cold, hard, bitter winter. The chill was not so much in the snow which lay on the Indiana hills as it was the frost in the hearts of young Sally and Abraham Lincoln, and in the heart of Tom Lincoln in the house from which had gone the light and life and lodestone. The daily routine went on, it was true. Folk ate and slept, and there was work to be done, trees to be cut, rails split, fences built; candles made, soap made, hominy made; washing to be finished and water to be carried up the long hill; food to be got somehow and kindling chopped. The Lincolns worked, but it all seemed without meaning, as if they moved in a dream, waiting hopefully to be awakened and find things as they were again, secure and comfortable because the presence of Nancy had meant all those things to those who loved her.

The winter went, and before it was time to plant again, Tom, in desperation and to break the spell of the long winter, break its monotony and its indecision, the waiting for something he could not explain, decided to go back to Kentucky and see his mother. Bathsheba Lincoln always had had a wise solution to most troubles. She had known so many in her life, had met them so firmly and with uplifted chin, daring fate to down her, that her children, in their own periods of grief and adversity, instinctively turned to her for help. Kentucky was not so far away, though to Tom it seemed, sometimes, as if the old life there was an eon away, not of this present world, but of a pleasant golden, youthful past. Yet only ninety-odd miles lay between the Indiana home which was no longer a home, to the home of his mother, which would never cease to be a haven while she lingered in it.

Bathsheba Lincoln had always appeared deceptively frail, a tiny thing only five feet tall when she was young, and she had shrunken to even less than that in her advancing age, to a wraith of a woman, yet she was amazingly strong and enduring. She was nearly seventy, and that was incredibly ancient in the wilderness where women wore out fast, and folk were aged before they were fifty. In the home of her youngest daughter, Nancy Brumfield, Bathsheba Lincoln lived on. Her neighbors revered her, her children loved her, and in her a far-off past lived again.

"Dennis, I want you should stay and look after things," ordered Tom Lincoln, putting up a lunch in a saddlebag and adding his shaving things and whatever else he figured he and the two children would need on a visit.

"You stick around, you hear? And don't let the varmints get at the stock. If I come back and find there's ary shoat or calf gone, I'll take it out of your hide, so help me!" He had to talk rough to Dennis. It was the only kind of talk that would sink in.

Dennis grinned that tantalizing grin which always made Tom want to shake him until his back teeth rattled.

"Sure, sure, Tom, I know what you're getting at. You don't need to have to worry none. I don't aim to stick so close I grow roots, but I'll guarantee you your precious stock'll be here when you come back—only don't stay too long 'cause I don't hanker to waste too much time as guard-een of your property. If you was half a man, you'd take me along!"

"Well, someone's got to stay. I ain't goin' off and leave all my stock and house and such to the mercy of whatever comes along. You stay, Dennis Hanks, and when I git back you kin go visitin' if you like, or go stay anywhere you want, for all of me. Only right now I got to go back and see Maw for a spell and git straightened out. Cain't go on like this for the rest of my life."

"Ought to git yourself another woman," said Dennis, his ugly face smirking. "That's what you need, and your young ones need a mammy to do for them. No way to live, way we been doin' lately. Like Injuns, 'cept we take an interest in religion and politics."

"You mind your own business, Dennis Hanks," flared Tom, reddening clear down his thick neck.

Even in early March, Kentucky looked good to Tom Lincoln when he, mounted on the proud Red Duke and followed by the two children on Maggie, the mare, rode up the road to the Beech Fork farm where Granny Basheby lived.

The brisk little old lady in the starched white cap cried out at the sight of them and came to meet them on toddling steps which were somehow as sturdy as ever. Bathsheba Lincoln never forgot a face or a voice, even back to Dan Boone and the folk she'd known when her husband, Captain Abraham Lincoln, had brought her and her five children up the Buffalo Trace and the Wilderness Road to the Indian-infested, wild Kentucky country. It had been a wrench to leave the kinder life she had known on the plantation in Virginia, but she had never really regretted giving it up. Even when Abraham had been killed by an Indian, and her oldest son, Mord, had used his father's own rifle gun to kill the murderer, and she was left alone, widowed, almost penniless, with five children to bring up, she had refused to retreat to Virginia. Lincolns never went back. They stuck it out or they went on and bettered themselves. She had stayed, and she had bettered herself, too, she liked to think. She had done a creditable job with her family.

Tom swooped on her and lifted her high, brought her down with a great kiss and hugged her. He hadn't realized how much he had missed his mother until now.

"Tommy!" she cried. "You're squeezing the life out of me! Where's Nancy? You didn't leave her at home did you? And Sally and little Abe—did you bring them?"

"Of course I brought the young ones, Maw," Tom said, pulling them out from where they had hid behind him. "But—but Nancy's been gone from us since last fall," he added soberly, gazing down at her with the hurt still in his eyes, the disbelief that it had really happened—as if he looked to her to assure him that it was all a dream. "Aunt Betsey and Uncle Tom went, too, and Aunt Lucy and Levi."

Bathsheba's mouth quivered. "I did hanker after Nancy," she said sadly. "I hoped she'd come and talk to me like she used to, sometimes; you never brought her often enough. Now she's gone, and what will you do, Tommy?"

She peered at the two children, who stared back at her.

"Land! They look fair neglected!" she chided. "Look at their hair. Seems like it's not been touched with a comb for weeks. And their clothes! Thomas Lincoln, they may not have a mammy but they do have a pappy, and I look to you to see to it they don't stay like this—like woodsies, or wild Indians with no manners or bringing up! A disgrace!" She bustled them into the house.

"Maw, do come and sit down," said handsome Nancy Brumfield as soon as she had greeted the newcomers. "Tom, she gets tired quick, so don't you keep her going too long. She's getting terrible feeble, seems like to me."

"I'm not feeble!" snorted Bathsheba Lincoln, the old fire in her eyes. "I may have lost my teeth and have to gum my vittles, and I may not see so well sometimes, and mayhap my ears play me tricks; but my wits are as sound as they ever were, and I'll thank you not to talk about me as if I were a post—saying I'm done for, a feeble old woman!"

Bathsheba sat down in a rocking chair, leaned her head back and closed her eyes for a moment, hunting patience.

"Maw, you got to rest now and not talk so much," put in Nancy Brumfield, worriedly. "We'll have dinner on soon." She hurried to get food for the company.

"Pay me no mind!" snapped Bathsheba, opening her keen eyes. "I'm as strong as I ever was. It just peters me out to have to drag my son along all the days of my life, because he hasn't the gumption to get up and do for himself!"

"Oh, Maw, I'm doin' all right," protested Tom, embarrassed at the way he, a man of forty, was being scolded and set down by this puny little mite who was his mother. He'd come hoping for sympathy from her, and she was only scolding him.

"It's up to you, Tom," she murmured. "I reckon you're old

enough to make up your mind what you want to do. I can't always do it for you." Her voice trailed off and she sat there rocking gently, her eyes closed, thinking back suddenly to the days long, long ago, when her husband, Abraham, tall and glorious to look at, had fought his way into the land of Kentucky. She thought back on Dan Boone and his wife, Rebecca, and their daughter, Jemima, all strong-willed, sturdy people who faced down the Indians and survived the wilderness . . . and of Adam Marlow and Jim Harrod and . . . The names slipped out of her grasp, and she could only see them hazily, as from a long way off, moving like wraiths through the forests of Kentucky, but, in her memory, shining with a kind of glory. Perhaps folk today had lost that dedicated light, that shining purpose. Maybe that was why some, like her poor Tom, could only try halfheartedly—and fail and fail and fail and no light would ever shine around them.

Tom left the children at Granny Basheby's house, to the delight of Bathsheba, in whose eyes Abe was the youthful embodiment of her husband—and to the joy of the children, who reveled in the attention, good food and comfortable beds, as well as the endless stories Bathsheba told them around the fire at night.

Tom Lincoln rode the Red Duke prancingly into Elizabethtown and down along the main street, to hunt up his old cronies at Crutcher's Store. Tom always presented quite an air of elegance when he was mounted on the fine red stallion. The Red Duke made another man of him, and being back in his old haunts was as good as a tonic to his spirits.

"Well, for the land's sake," said a clear voice, that first day he was back in town, "if it isn't Tom Lincoln! Why, Tom, I thought you'd gone away for good!"

Tom wheeled the Red Duke.

"Sally—why Sally Bush! Howdy, howdy!" he cried, whipping off his hat with a fine flourish. "Yes, I'm back, just on a visit, though. I guess you ain't heard—Nancy's dead—she died last fall of the milksick. It was bad up in Indiana. I brought the young ones back to visit their granny for a few days before spring plantin'.

"How are things with you, ma'am?" he added politely.

"My husband's gone, too, Tom," she said softly, looking down with a saddening of her pleasant face which, in spite of the years and tribulations—in spite of scrubbing the jail and somehow managing to bring up three children and nurse an ailing husband—still was rosy and fresh-looking.

"He died a little while after you went to Indiana, Tom. I'm sorry about your wife. I always liked Nancy; everybody did. She was a right good woman. You living alone over there now?"

"Yes, 'cept for that Dennis Hanks who I could do without," said Tom bitterly. "It's a lone, hard life without a woman—and I reckon that for you it's just as bad, if not worse. I'm sure sorry, Sally."

Then other friends came along, and the conversation ended. Or it seemed to end, though something unseen and unspoken had passed between the two.

Thomas Lincoln went back to the cheerless home in Indiana. Abe and Sally hated to leave their cousins because it was such fun playing with them, hated to leave Aunt Nancy Brumfield's excellent cooking, her comfortable beds and her loving care of them, and hated most of all, perhaps, to leave the little old lady in the rocking chair. Having a grandmother to fuss over them had been a heady experience.

In silence the three Lincolns rode all the chill, miserable rainy March way home to Indiana—rode up the sticky clay hills and slogged down into the hollows where the horses pulled through with an effort and the yellow mud splashed over them, and finally up the last hill to the cabin.

Dennis Hanks, for a wonder, was there, doubtless kept in by the rain. He had a fire going, but the cabin nevertheless seemed lonely and cold, an unhappy place because there was no loving woman there to welcome them and take off their hoods and shawls and warm them with love and kindness and food. This was not a house that a woman had cared for and kept clean and comfortable.

Dennis had not burned down the place, but he had evidently not touched a broom. Trash and bones littered the dirt floor. He'd upset a crock of milk and, though the liquid had sunk into the earth of the floor, it still smelled sour. Abe and Sally crawled into their uncomfortable pole beds and tried to get warm, while Tom roundly laid it into Dennis, who was sullen and would not talk. All in all, it was not a happy homecoming. Sally cried a little into her bedding, and Abe wrapped his thin arms around himself and hunched up into a knot. He was shivery and miserable and unhappy, not just because he was cold, but because he was lonesome for something he couldn't name, but which was there in Aunt Nancy's house where old Granny Basheby lived.

As he lay there, he remembered what Granny Basheby had said to him just before he left. She had asked him to come close, to kneel on the floor so she could look into his gray eyes from where she sat. She had looked so deeply into his eyes that he had grown uncomfortable, and she had smiled, then.

"It's all right, Abe," she had said softly, patting his hands. "I just wanted to see if it was still there. You haven't lost it."

Tom Lincoln never made up his mind to anything very quickly. It took him all spring and all summer and all autumn to decide, while he halfheartedly planted and cultivated and harvested the crop of the year 1819. And as he worked he worried about the rough appearance of the Red Duke and feared that the wilds of Indiana were not the place for a Kentucky thoroughbred. If anything happened to the Red Duke—

It was the last week in November before Tom made up his mind. Then he didn't consult anyone about it. He just up and said one morning at breakfast:

"I'm goin' to be gone a couple days, and I want you three to mind and take care of things and not get into no trouble. If you need help, go down to the Crawfords'. Abe, take care you behave and mind what Sally tells you to do. Your sister has had it hard all this year, cookin' for three menfolk like she's done, so don't make it no harder for her than it is."

"Where're you goin', Paw?" asked Abe, looking up at his father, who was unusually spruce and neat.

"I'll let you know when I'm of a mind to!" answered Tom, flushing.

"Good-bye, Paw," said Sally. "I'll take care of things."

"I know you will, honey," said Tom with unaccustomed tenderness, and he bent suddenly and kissed her on the forehead.

A week later, Dennis was in Rockport and Abe and Sally were alone in the untidy, dark and smelly cabin. It was uncomfortable and they were hungry, but an overwhelming discouragement and loneliness had risen like a tide in both children so that neither had the incentive to fix food or clean the house. A rumbling and rattling and creaking out on the road brought them to their feet, questions in their eyes, looking at each other.

"Who do you suppose?" cried Sally. "It couldn't be Paw—he hasn't a wagon."

But it was Paw—Paw and a whole passel of people, filling a wagon drawn by a yoke of oxen.

Abe and Sally stood in the open doorway, but hung back, shy and scared, as the wagon pulled up to the cabin and stopped. It was a handsome Conestoga with a flapping canvas cover tied down all around except in front and back, and drawn by mottled brown oxen. The animals were blowing, and their breaths came in clouds of vapor on the wintery air.

Tom Lincoln, beaming and joyful, jumped from the wagon and helped a woman down. Behind her peered three children, two girls and a boy. Sally and Abe, wordless, stood and watched.

"Well, what're you waitin' for, you young ones—come out and meet your new mother! I been and brought you a new mother and two new sisters and a brother. How do you like that, hey?" He was overdoing it, grinning and talking loudly in the nervousness he felt at how they would take it, though they had naught to say in the matter, since it was all his doing, and for their own good, if they would but see it so.

The woman smiled, but stood where she was. She had pink cheeks and dark hair showed under her bonnet. She looked tall and fine in her gray bombazine gown and her fringed shawl. She just stood and smiled gently at Abe and at Sally. Almost as if pulled by invisible strings, still wordless, the two crept out, barefoot and ragged and uncombed and dirty, to where the woman stood. She placed a hand on the shoulder of each child. Suddenly she bent and laid a kiss on Sally's cheek and then on Abe's.

"Dears, I know I can't take your real mother's place, but I'll try. I've seen you often in Elizabethtown, and now I'm happy to be here with you. These here are my three young ones—Elizabeth, get down and make your manners. This is my oldest, Elizabeth Johnston, she's twelve, the same as you, Sally. This is Matilda—do watch that wheel, Tilda, it's high. Tilda's eight, and she's a great tease, Abe. And John D. is the youngest. He's only four, Abe, so you'll have to teach him things."

Abe recollected suddenly where he'd seen this woman with the kind face. She was Mis Johnston, the jailor's wife. He'd seen her sometimes when he was in town with Paw and recollected that John D. was a squawling young one, always hanging on to her skirts. From Abe's superior age of ten years, John D. still looked pretty much a baby and not worth much. Abe couldn't quite figure out how this Mis Johnston could now be his new mother, but he guessed Paw had fixed it up some way.

He smiled a quick, small, polite smile up at Mis Johnston. Sally was looking at her soberly, her thin face not cracking a smile, just gazing in a detached way, as if perhaps she didn't like what Paw had done.

"Well, what're you waitin' for?" snapped Tom, impatient in his nervousness. "Can't you say howdy to your new mammy? Go on, say it! Don't act like you ain't got no manners!"

"Howdy, ma'am," said Abe shyly, his big gray eyes taking in her smooth, silky-looking gown and the black mitts on her hands. His own mother had never had anything half so fine.

Just then Tobias, the hound, having suddenly awakened to what was going on, belatedly began to bark and bay, which broke the tension. Tom threw a chunk at the dog, who retired in confusion into the house.

"Come on, come on, get inside. It's cold out here, and we got to git vittles on for supper. I reckon you're hungry, Sally," Tom exclaimed.

He wasn't looking at his daughter, Sally, when he said it, but at the new stepmother, and Sally Lincoln felt a twinge of hideous pain at her heart to hear Paw say her name like that to someone else. She stumbled after the others into the dark, smelly cabin.

With a bitter joy, she saw how Sarah Bush Johnston Lincoln looked comprehensively and with horror around the cabin with its meager furnishings and its air of palpable neglect.

"Heaven's mercy, Tom Lincoln!" Sarah cried, shocked. "You rightly do need a woman! Here—you get my things out of the wagon before the night dampness ruins them, and I'll see to fixing food. What's in the house to eat, Sally?"

"Nothin' much," answered Sally glumly.

"Oh, there must be something!" Sarah said briskly, refusing to be vanquished at the outset by the sullen Lincoln children and the unspeakable hovel to which Tom had brought her and her own children. Food and a good fire would make all the difference.

"Bring in more wood, Abe—build up that fire, Tom," she commanded, taking off her bonnet and gaily tying on a big apron. She found cornmeal and mixed up cornbread which she set to bake on the hearth. Then she sliced up some pork for the skillet, started a pot of coffee to cooking, found some dried pumpkin chips which she softened in hot water and set to cooking quickly with salt and maple sugar, for sauce. It was, she found, about all the food in the house, and it was, she discovered, the last of the coffee.

"It's not much," she declared, sitting them down to food in a little while, "but it'll stay us till tomorrow when I can get things to rights and know where we stand. Tom, be sure to bring in my bureau-chest and chairs before they get ruined . . . and the rest of my things, too."

The bureau-chest was wonderful to see. It was smooth as the polished maple gunstock on Paw's Kentucky rifle and had drawers which moved in and out. Oh, it was beautiful! It gave the cabin quite an air to have it just standing there against the log wall. The new mother brought in her featherbeds and everyone fixed up beds on the floor for the night—till proper beds could be set up, she said. It was too late to work with tightening ropes and setting up the beds that came from the big wagon.

When Dennis came staggering in late that night, he almost stepped on Elizabeth Johnston and her sister Tilda in the middle of the floor. Abe chuckled under his breath until tears ran down his cheeks at how surprised Denny was, with too much spirits under his belt and now finding all the new kinfolk come to stay and no place for him to bed down except up in the loft—and it was right cold up there. Dennis slipped on the ladder rungs and barked his shin, and cussed out loud something awful.

Abe heard Tom hiss, "Cut out the cussin', Dennis Hanks, we got company!" At that, Abe burst into a whoop which set the rest of the children to laughing, too. Tom roared at all of them and they finally quieted down.

Meanwhile, Dennis managed to get himself up to the loft. They heard him bumping around up there, but finally all was quiet. Out in the barn the oxen quietly champed. It was then that Abe thought of something. He wondered if he dared call to Paw about it now, and then decided he'd better not. He'd wait and ask tomorrow.

He cornered his father out in the barn the next morning.

"Paw," he demanded, bracing himself in case Tom decided to whale into him, as he sometimes did when Abe asked questions which irritated him. "Paw, where-at is the Red Duke?"

Tom looked at him quickly, and Abe could see a certain hurt in his father's eyes which he hadn't seen there before. Tom did not whale into him. He just slumped down a little and said:

"I had to sell the Red Duke, Abe. I purely hated to, but there was naught else to do. The Duke was kin to the mare my own pappy rode over the mountains on, but I had to sell that stallion. I got a good price for him over to Lexington, and glad to get it. There was naught else to do," he repeated unhappily. "When I went and asked Mis Johnston would she be my wife, she said yes, thank you, 'cept I have debts I can't pay, and she would never up and marry me until they was settled.

"So, I said, well, that's what I'm here for. I'll pay all your just debts from now on. Only I hadn't very much cash money, as you know, and the only thing I had to sell of any worth was the poor Red Duke. It purely hurt to part with him, that I'm tellin' you, Son. The Duke was like my own blood kin. But he'll do well over in Lexington, among his own kind. He was too fine for the backwoods here, and I've always been afeered he'd die of some ailment I couldn't cure, or might be stole from me and mistreated. Now he'll be where he belongs, back in Kentucky. I paid Mis Johnston's debts, bought the wagon and oxen off of Ralph Crume, your Aunt Mary's husband, and there's a little to spare. We was wed in Elizabethtown on December second, Abe. I trust you get on well with your new mammy. She's a right fine woman, and I couldn't do no better for my young ones than ask for a mammy like her."

"Our own mammy was fine enough," defended Abe, hurt at how quickly Paw was forgetting.

"Sure she was," Tom agreed hastily, still not whaling into the boy, who was braced for a clip over the ear. "But we ain't got her now. You be good to your new mammy, Abe, and she'll be good to you all the days of her life."

Then Tom Lincoln went about his chores, hating the sight of the stolid brown ox in the stall which used to belong to the glossy, spirited, handsome Red Duke.

CHAPTER ELEVEN

Times in the Lincoln household were definitely changed.

"Tom Lincoln," said Sarah the next day, not in anger, but sweetly and firmly, hands on hips, laughing a little, "when I agreed to wed you and care for you and your young ones, I never figured I'd have to do it in a pigpen, and I won't! It's time you pulled yourself together and got busy on this house. You and Dennis whipsaw enough planks to make a nice floor. The idea, no floor! We've got to have us a floor to keep us warm and clean. I'll make some rag rugs first chance I get. And next time there are lime burners in the neighborhood, you get enough lime to make a mess of whitewash. You and the boys can whiten the walls and ceiling so we'll look neat and it'll not be so dark in here, either. Get some good slabs of rock and make a hearth, and we've surely got to have more furnishings, beds and the like, for all of us. These makeshifts may have been all right when you were just a-building and getting started, but it's time you finished the job right."

"Yes, Sally—" said Tom meekly, and was cut off by her firm voice.

"Call me Sarah, please, Tom. We can't have two of us called Sally in one household!" And she smiled over at Sally Lincoln, who looked up, startled to find how the woman had read her mind.

"Oh, all right," agreed Tom impatiently, thinking of all the work she had laid out for him, but he admitted to himself that he needed someone to push him like this, so he'd get it done. Nancy'd always let him do as he pleased.

While Tom was carpentering in Elizabethtown, long ago, he'd done good work when he was working for someone else, but in his own house he was always letting it go until later, and never getting around to jobs that stared him in the face. Might be he could find time to make Sarah a fine corner cupboard, or some such knickknack to please her, after they got the floor laid and the hearth and the whitewashing done, and all such—if she didn't keep on getting more ideas.

Yes, things were mightily different around the Lincoln place. Before Abe got up, the second morning, Sarah energetically demanded his worn and dirty garments and, looking them over with considerable distaste, at arm's length, decided they were beyond washing and mending. Out they went to be burned in the big fire where she was destroying the trash that cluttered the house and yard. Abe, huddling under the quilts of his bed, was embarrassed and miserable. She'd given him a hot scrub-bath, with lots of soap that got into his eyes and stung like the mischief. She'd cut his hair after it was washed and worked the rats' nests out of it, cleaned out his fingernails and trimmed them and even his toenails. He was getting more and more embarrassed at what this woman was up to. When she burned up his only suit of clothes, he felt like crying, but young, impudent John D., dressed decently and clean, was making faces at him, so he didn't cry.

"Don't you worry a mite, Abe," soothed Sarah, seeing his anguish. "I'll whip you up a new shirt and pants in a hurry. You're so tall, I might cut down a pair of these old breeches I brought along, thinking I might make them over later for John D., but looks to me like you ought to have them. Now you lay there— Here," she added, fishing into a bureau drawer, "you look at this book—you can read, can't you?—and that'll make the time pass. I sew fast, Abe." She smiled at him, understanding his unhappiness, and smiled, too, at how quickly he forgot his grief at sight of the book.

"Thank you, ma'am," he said shyly—and was lost in the magic of the *Arabian Nights,* lost in a world he had never dreamed of in his life.

Somehow, the two families got settled together. Somehow they got themselves fitted and dovetailed into each other's ways, and life went on. And it was a good life, with Sarah Lincoln always there to talk and joke and cook good food and make clothes and do the work, and make the best of the sometimes meager fixings which she often had to do with. She met the neighbors and they liked her, though Elizabeth Crawford, who came calling one day shortly after the new Mrs. Lincoln's presence was discovered in the Little Pigeon Creek neighborhood, thought it odd that the Lincolns had so little to offer guests. There never had been much, she knew, but this—

Serene Sarah, however, was not embarrassed.

"Do come in, Mis Crawford," she said politely. "Make yourself comfortable. Here, take this cane-bottom chair. I brought it all the way from Kentucky when we came, and I'd admire to see how you like it."

Quickly, Sarah cast about in her mind as to what she could offer this fine neighbor, this brisk little woman with the keen blue eyes which saw through everything with gentleness, understanding, and no nonsense. She was attracted by the quizzical mouth, the busy hands that went at their knitting as soon as her guest was seated.

There wasn't much in the house. Sarah, in desperation, got out some raw sweet potatoes and pared them neatly, and brought them, with knives, to the table, while she brewed some dittany tea for her guest. With China tea at two dollars a pound, wild tea would have to do for the Lincolns, and they hadn't been able to buy coffee, either, for a while.

The two sat and cut slivers of the sweet potatoes and ate them genteelly and sipped the hot tea and talked, just as if they had been fine ladies in town with real Imperial tea and little cakes, thought Elizabeth Crawford, her mouth quirking in the corners when she thought of how different it was when Amanda Cissna Pitcher invited her in to have refreshment. Amanda Pitcher had real bone china that came all the way from England, and she had silver spoons and loaf sugar that had been wrapped in blue paper to keep it white, and lovely little cakes which her Negro cook baked in a real oven. But Amanda Cissna Pitcher, for all her fine gowns and fine house and fine fixings, Elizabeth concluded honestly, was no more truly hospitable than poor Mis Tom Lincoln the second, receiving her caller in a log cabin that hadn't a floor yet because her husband was shiftless, and serving wild dittany tea in pewter cups and sliced raw sweet potatoes, for want of anything better.

CHAPTER TWELVE

ABRAHAM LINCOLN was thirteen when James Swaney opened a subscription school, four miles up the road, in a rough-built little log house put up by the men of the Pigeon Creek Community. It was meagerly furnished with all the equipment that any school was considered to need. This consisted of a chair and a high desk for the teacher, backless benches for the pupils, a broom to stand behind the door, a water bucket and a gourd for drinking purposes, and a fireplace. It would be the big boys' job to keep the fireplace fueled with wood, which they were sent out to cut, and to keep the water bucket filled. There was one window. Unless the weather was too cold, the door and window stayed open to let in light and air.

There had been a brief period of school some time before, when Andrew Crawford taught not only the prescribed studies but manners and morals as well; but Mr. Crawford did not stay, and there was a long blank in which there was no teacher at all. Tom Lincoln, with Sarah's conniving, scraped up enough cash to send Abe, Tilda and Sally to Mr. Crawford, for a while, and when Mr. Swaney came along, Tom managed enough for Abe, Tilda and John D. for a month. At three dollars a pupil per month, that was a lot of money. Elizabeth said she was too old; she and Dennis were making plans to be married after a while, while Sally had her eye on Aaron Grigsby. Tom Lincoln was thankful there were only three young ones to send to school. As it was, he didn't see how he'd ever find enough ready money to send them longer when the first month was up.

Mr. James Swaney, a freckled, lanky, red-haired man of middle age, who had migrated from Ireland and somehow had found his way to the backwoods of Indiana, had had a little schooling himself, enough, he felt, to keep him a few jumps ahead of his brightest pupils.

But he did not take into account a certain pupil who drove him distracted with questions. Abe Lincoln was smart. He could read better than the others and he could recite in such a long-winded manner that Mr. Swaney had to hush him up in order to give the others a chance to take their halting turns and offer his own eardrums a rest. It was a noisy school anyway, because Mr. Swaney, like many another educator of that day, believed that if pupils recited their lessons aloud, in unison, then he would be sure they were studying, and were keeping their minds on their work. If they were studying aloud, they weren't whispering to each other. In fact, a whisper would have been lost in the daily racket of a blab-school. But Mr. Swaney felt he could stand the roar of study better than the words of that talkative Abraham Lincoln, when he got himself up to recite and then went on to repeat half the book from memory, with fine gestures of his big hands and arms, as learned from *The Kentucky Preceptor.*

"Oh, go set down, Aberham," James Swaney would say tiredly, rapping on his desk with his ferule. "I didn't ask you should repeat the whole of the book when I asked you to give me the boundaries of the United States. Set down!"

Abe, disappointed because he couldn't say all he knew, folded himself up and sat down. He was getting so tall that he always felt like a cricket folding up its legs to get ready to jump, whenever he had to sit down on the uncomfortable puncheon bench. It was all right, though; he was learning. There was a chance at a few more books than he'd seen elsewhere, and he was getting to be a fair hand with a goose-quill pen, so folk could read what he wrote without squinting.

At the end of the first month of school that fall, however, Tom Lincoln passed his ultimatum.

"Well, your young ones and mine have had their education for this time, Sarah," he decreed. "I ain't got the money to pay for the next month, and that's the gospel truth. If that Swaney would only board around, it wouldn't cost me so much. But I ain't got the money to send three of 'em next month, no matter what it costs. I wish I could, I truly do," he added honestly, "but I just cain't afford it."

Abe heard and his heart sank.

"Well, but Paw," he protested, "we just got to get some money somewhere! I'm just gettin' a good start, and I'm nowhere near ready to quit yet. Tilda's doin' right good, too, and even John D.'s learned to read a little and can almost write his name so you can read it good. Paw, we got to keep on! I'll find a way—if I can earn the money, can we go?"

Tom scowled at him. "You're always hankerin' for somethin' you ain't got, Abe Lincoln," he said. "If you was to get more satisfied with your place in life and didn't try to git up to where you got no rightful business, you'd be better off. *I'm* satisfied, or pretty near. I don't aim to rise above my station. I know when I'm well off, and you better be like me, I say. But anyways, if I could afford to give you an education, I'd humor you and let you have it, I certain would!"

Abe hadn't the slightest idea as to how to earn enough money to send three children to school for another month. Nine dollars was a lot of money. He sometimes earned a few cents by working for Josiah Crawford or Judge Turnham, but at that rate he'd never get enough in time. It would have to be a big chunk of money, all in a lump.

"We can't use the goose feathers," Sarah said sadly. "We'll need the money from them this winter. The corn didn't do so well this year, and—well, I honestly don't know where you'll get it, Abe."

Abe was sitting on the doorstep, absently drawing pictures in the dust and trying to get an idea in his head, when something zoomed past and he instinctively ducked. It was the season for the big cicada-killer wasps, and he knew that if they stung you, you were pretty sick afterwards and maybe died, they were so poisonous. But this was a lighter-weight zoom and buzz, not so mean-sounding. He looked up in time to see a honeybee, heavy with goldenrod pollen, pause on a sunflower nearby, and then take off, traveling heavily toward the woods.

"Bees!" If he could find him a real good bee tree . . . Abe was up and off through the dust of the clearing, his head high, keeping track of the bee. He caught up with it when it paused on another goldenrod stalk, then it took off into the woods with Abe still after it. He had a time following. He couldn't take the usual deer trails, because the pesky bee didn't, but went in the proverbial beeline, with no concern for the boy who was loping after it. The pea vines were at their toughest and most matted, strong with all the burgeoning of the long summer. They caught him around the ankles and threw him down. When he scrambled up he thought he'd lost the bee, but he could still see it, and kept on. He stumbled and was tangled again in the terrible little vines which looked so innocent and were so strong. His bare feet stung and his ankles burned with the friction of the vines across them as he ran. He just had to catch up with that bee!

Head in the air, watching anxiously, he didn't see the fallen branch of an old beech. It caught him across the shins, raking the skin, and threw him headlong. He measured his length on the forest floor.

He sat up, shaking the dirt off his shirt, worriedly listening and looking for the bee, but he had lost it at last. It was nowhere in sight, and his keen ears, attuned always to the voices of the forest, could not detect its buzzing and humming. He wearily got to his feet and stumbled on in the direction in which he had been going, with not much hope in his heart of finding what he sought. . . . He stopped suddenly and listened.

There it was, a low-pitched, concerted thrumming, as if a whole lot of bees had gathered under a washtub. They were inside some-thing—that was certain—and out here the only thing they'd be in was a hollow tree. It would be full of honey!

His energy renewed, Abe bounded in the direction of the sound, and, deep in the woods, he came upon a big old beech tree. Its purple-gray trunk was scarred with bear scratches and the rubbings made by buck deer when their antlers were in the velvet and had to be scraped off sharp and clean—the scars of all the long years in the life of the old beech were on it. About fifteen feet up there was a big opening where a large bough had broken off long ago, and the heart of the tree had thereupon rotted out, until it was only a shell, but with enough life left in it to put out leaves every year. The roaring of the bees was loud in there, and the boy could see the insects coming and going through the shafts of shining, dusty autumn sunlight which filtered through the deeply layered canopy of glowing autumn leaves. There was a sort of translucent golden sheen in the atmosphere of the forest, dominated by the humming of hundreds of bees.

Abe had been running so far into the woods with his head in the air and not paying attention to direction or to locations of trails he knew that he wasn't at all sure where he was. He listened, trying to catch some familiar sound. But there was nothing, no sound at all in the lovely autumn day but the humming of the bees and the remote cheepings of robins eating red haws. He heard a turkey churking and talking to itself and saw a hen come up to the bee tree and peck around for the ripening beech nuts among the leaves. The gobbler and three more hens and some young ones hatched that spring came up, too, paying no attention to Abe as he slumped on a fallen log to rest and catch his breath until he had found his bearings.

It was ineffably still and lonely in that part of the forest. Abe couldn't remember ever having been there before. It was somewhere down in the lowlands, he knew. Up in the hill woods, he could always hear the wind moving through the leaves and making the twigs talk; he could hear all sorts of small sounds, creatures stirring the leaves on the ground, a smell of pennyroyal strong when he crushed it underfoot, the song of a thrush or the whistling of a towhee, and always that talking of the wind in the trees.

But down in these bottomland woods, it was so silent. The turkeys moved off, and even the bees seemed to pause in their humming, and he could not hear the robins cheeping any more. It was as if the whole world stood still and was completely mute, watching him, enveloped in autumn silence that stretched north to the top of the world. It was an almost frightening soundlessness; it made a fellow want to snap his fingers or whistle, or something, to break the spell.

The trees were huge and quiet, their leaves so motionless; there was no talking of the wind, for none moved that autumn day. Then a vireo set up a disconnected conversation. A squirrel in the distance chattered, and Abe was somehow thankful to hear it. The bees were humming again, and off in the distance a big woodpecker —must be a logcock, it sounded so loud—tunk-tunked resonantly on a hollow tree.

The sun was slanting definitely to westward beyond the trees, so he figured that if he started east, he would come out near his father's land, but he walked until nearly sundown before he found it.

Sarah was getting supper on the table when he burst into the house.

"Maw, I've found me a bee tree!" he rejoiced. "It's a great big old hollow beech out in the woods west of here, an awful big and lonely woods. I've never even seen it before. If I can find that tree again, we sure will have honey and beeswax to sell! Paw," he said, turning to where Tom had looked up at him, inquiringly, from where he sat by the fire, mending a pair of moccasins. "Paw, can I have the borrow of the mare and the sled to haul honey tomorrow? I reckon there's a lot there."

"Well, Abe," said Tom judiciously, squinting at the moccasin. "I don't know if I can let you have that honey. It's rightfully mine, since you're under age, you know, and I need the money as bad as you do, if not more so, seeing the taxes and land payments will be due. You show me whereat that bee tree is, and we'll go out and get the honey tomorrow, if it don't rain. I always did hanker to find me a bee tree around here but never got around to it."

Abe could feel an insufferable sensation of hatred and unhappiness rising like a tide inside himself. It was his bee tree, his honey, and he just *had* to sell it so he and Tilda and John D. could keep on a while longer at Swaney's blab-school.

"Paw!" he protested, "It's my honey! I found it. I've just got to have the money for school, and I don't know any other way to get some—"

"Don't talk back to me, Abraham Lincoln!" thundered Tom, getting up. "You're my son, and whatever you got belongs to me till you're twenty-one. When you're of age, you got a right to branch out for yourself and keep what you earn. That's my honey, I say, and I'll do with it what I want! And the wax, too."

Sarah put down her stirring spoon and looked at her husband.

"Thomas Lincoln, I'm fair ashamed of you," she said sadly, her eyes boring uncomfortably into him. "I didn't know you could be so stingy. If I had, I doubt me that I'd ever have chanced it to wed you!" And she turned to stirring the hominy again, her bent back righteous with disapproval.

Tom squirmed. "You got no call to talk like that, Sarah," he protested, vexed at her and, unwillingly, at himself. "I only mentioned my rights. Way things is goin' nowadays, I sometimes wonder if a father got any rights left at all. Young ones speakin' up and all such, no respect in them for their betters, demandin' this and demandin' that. . . ."

"Abe only wants an education, and the bee tree ought to be rightfully his to give him some money to help him out," she said distantly, simply stating the facts as she saw them.

Tom squirmed again. He spat in the fire.

"Don't spit in the fire when I'm cooking vittles over it!" she snapped at him.

"All right, all right," he muttered. "Everyone's ag'in me. You go on and get your honey, Abe Lincoln, but you got to do it all yourself and don't ask me for no help. And I require you give me half of what you git from the sale of that honey. The wax you do with as you want!"

"Can't I use the mare and the sugar sled to haul it?" asked Abe warily.

Tom was about to say no, firmly, but Sarah beat him to it and answered:

"Of course you can, Abe. Your paw was just about to say that. And your paw was only joking about giving him half your money. You sell that honey and wax and see how far the money'll go in school. I reckon since John D. don't hanker for it much, he wouldn't have to keep on this time, if there wasn't enough money."

Next morning Abe hurried to get Allen Brooner and David Turnham to help him with the honey project. While they were still at the Turnhams', Ann Roby, who'd been visiting Mary Turnham, begged to go along, too.

"It's too dangerous for girls," stated Abraham firmly, walking faster toward the Crawfords' place. "Come on, fellows, we got a long way to go."

"But I want to go with you and see the bee tree and help you get the honey!" protested Ann, tagging along.

"You go back and play dolls with Mary," Allen shouted over his shoulder. "This is man's work!"

David grinned. "She'll get tired taggin'," he vowed, "when she finds out how far she has to go. You reckon you know the way in, Abe?"

"Sure I do," he said, swinging the wooden tub on to the sled at the Crawfords'.

"How're you goin' to get the horse and sled way in there, if there ain't no trails?" asked Allen dubiously. He carried a gourd with a chunk of fire inside it, to make a smudge when they found the tree.

"Well," Abe paused to think. He doubted if the mare would like tracking through all those pea vines and over the brush he had traveled through when he followed the bee. He paused in the cool dust of the bottomland road, in the shade of a silver maple tree whose leaves were still green.

"Let me think a minute," he said. He got a stick and began to draw a sort of map in the dust. The boys crowded around to look over his shoulder. Ann Roby, pert and pretty in a linsey gown, with her brown feet bare, caught up with them again and looked, too. Abe glanced up, exasperated.

"I told you to go back, Annie," he said, not unkindly, but firmly.

"But I want to go along!"

"Well, you can't! You run on back now, fast, or I'll send and tell your maw and paw, and they won't like you taggin' after boys!"

Ann turned and flounced down the road, but soon stepped quickly off into the bushes and waited, watching the boys from a distance. She saw them bending over the map-thing Abe was drawing in the dust.

"Now here is where I live." Abe pointed with his stick to a little square on the map. "And this here is where I figure the bee tree is, on a line southwest of the house, or somewhere mighty close, and a long way out in the woods. Well, now look, here is the deer trail. It seems to me, if we take the mare and the sled and tubs down the deer trail, and then go on over to the left about here, we'd ought to hit the tree. Come on, let's go!"

Maggie, the mare, didn't much relish the notion of dragging the sled, which was used to haul maple sap, along the narrow deer trail. From this path her sensitive nostrils continually detected strange and alarming scents from other creatures which had lately passed there and left their inerasable odors—the odors of panther and bear and skunk and fox and wolf. These were combined in a wild aroma which a human nose did not pick out above the rich mingling of scents filling the autumn woods, but which the mare's nostrils detected with agonizing surety. Her feet dragged and she hung back in the traces, as if reluctant to go a step further, until urged onward by the eager boys. The deer trail wound through the upland woods and then dipped down to the creek bottom and veered to cross the ford. It was just here, Abe had figured, that they should turn sharply to the left and take out into the pea vines and nettles to the old beech.

Maggie disliked this even more than she did the animal trail. The vines caught around her hocks and she had to pull loose and shake them free with every step. The sled slid easily over them, and the boys took turns riding to keep from having to navigate the pea vines. The nettles were bad in the bottoms, too, not having been knocked down by frost. The sun bore down, with its October strength undiminished by the nearness of winter, and laid an enervating heat down through the autumn colors of the leaves.

The boys were perspiring and the mare blew through her nostrils. From time to time the lure of honey-getting seemed considerably less to Allen and David, but to Abe, whose immediate schooling depended upon it, the venture did not lose its excitement and delight.

It was not so simple, however, to cut through the woods and find the bee tree.

Abe was beginning to get mightily discouraged. In the whole great forest there was at least one tree he pined to see. It seemed to him, though, that he was coming upon every single other tree in the woods but a scarred beech with its insides humming with bees—a tree set in a silent, remote forest which was somehow different from the rest of the woods. Every time he spotted the unmistakable form of a beech from a distance, he yelled that there it was, there was his tree, but it never had any bees in it. One had a hole in its side, and Allen insisted he could hear humming, but when he climbed up and put his head in, he took it out again in a hurry.

"Hey!" he yelled. "There's an old she-coon up here and she mighty nigh bit off my nose! I've a mind to wring her neck!"

"Aw, come on down," said Abe in disgust. "You always think you have to kill every livin' thing that disagrees with you. That old she-coon likely would tear you to ribbons before you ever got her out far enough to finish her off, even if you were man enough to do it. That ain't our tree. Come on down. It's gettin' late and I promised my paw I'd help with shockin' the corn this afternoon. I have to hurry back or have a lickin'."

Well, they found the tree at last, right where it had been all the time. They had walked circles around it for an hour before they heard the potent humming.

It was no small piece of work to chop down the beech. The big double-bitted ax which Abe swung knocked big white chips out of the old tree. Because beech wood is fairly soft, the ax eventually ate through to the notch and the boys stood back as, with a sort of murmuring within itself, the old tree slowly pivoted a little and went down. The bees swarmed out in a mighty fluster at the demolition of their castle. Allen made a smudge which dazed those which remained. The honey was oozing upon the ground, but inside the trunk there was a great mass of old and new honeycomb, filled with the luscious gleanings of last summer's flowers. The boys dug it out with their hands and piled it into the tubs, until the three were dripping and horribly sticky. The first few licks tasted wonderful, but in a little while they grew tired of the cloying sweetness and only wanted a drink of water and a chance to jump in the creek and wash off.

Abe kept them working, though, until they had all the good comb heaped in the wooden tubs. Then the trio drove the mare carefully through the woods and along the deer trail, to the creek, where they let her drink. They drank, too, and then stripped and went in to wash off the honey and dead leaves and dirt that had stuck to them.

Down where the rocks went across the ford, Abe noted tracks in the mud. They were small, humanlike tracks—like a child's, maybe. Nobody lived for miles around here and he couldn't figure out why there would be footprints in this spot, but soon he let the wondering slip from his mind. The boys got the sled started up the hill, bracing the tubs so they wouldn't go sliding off and spilling the precious, hard-earned honey. A few bees that had escaped the smoking came tagging along, lighting on the stuff sometimes, and Allen, in brushing them away, was stung over the eye, which promptly swelled shut. Abe got a sting on the calf of his leg which hurt like fury and made him limp. He got up on Maggie, the mare, to ride the rest of the way.

Sarah and John D. and Tilda and Dennis and Elizabeth all came out to view the three tubs of honey. The children stuck their fingers into the sweet stuff and licked them and exclaimed over how good it was—they hadn't had any honey since last year.

"What'm I goin' to do with it, Maw?" asked Abe in perplexity, wondering how to store the three sticky tubs, now that he had them. He'd have to borrow the Crawfords' wagon and take the honey to town tomorrow, but meanwhile, he couldn't just leave it out here in the yard. It would attract all the bears for miles around, and he wouldn't have a drop of honey left by morning.

"It's too dusty in the barn," Abe went on, figuring. "Maw, could I bring the tubs into the house if I wipe up the drips and get them out tomorrow?"

"Well, I guess there's no help for it," said Sarah reluctantly, "but I don't want to find a single drop of that sticky honey on my clean floor or anywhere else in the house after you've taken them out! Now get them in here quick and go on out to the field. Your paw's been growling around about you not coming to help. It's hours till supper, so you've got plenty time. What's the matter with your leg?" she added, noting how he limped.

"Bee sting."

"Well, I wish you didn't have to go to work, but the best thing for a bee sting is to keep moving so's the poison don't have a chance to act. Anyway, you'd have to be a whole lot worse hurt for your paw to let you off!"

It was while Abe was reading by the fire that night, lying flat on his back with his head pillowed on a chunk of wood, his hair dangerously near the blaze, so he'd get enough light, that there came a pounding on the door. It was Absolem Roby, Judge Turnham and Bill Barker. They had torches, and their horses stood waiting in the yard.

"Evenin', Tom," Absolem said worriedly, when Tom Lincoln threw open the door. "No, we can't come in. There's work to be done. Annie's lost. We got to find her before it gets any later, with all them wolves and panthers around in these here woods. Abe," Roby said anxiously to the boy, who, startled, had put his book down and sat up. "Mary Turnham says Annie was determined she'd go with you-all to find the bee tree. Did she?"

Abe shook his head. Knowing Ann Roby, he ought to have realized she wouldn't take no for an answer when they wouldn't let her go along, but he hadn't given her another thought after she turned around. If she'd followed anyway . . . and he knew suddenly and positively that she had.

"No, Mr. Roby," said Abe slowly, thinking hard. "She up and pestered us to go along, but we told her no, she couldn't, and last I seen of here she was goin' back toward Turnhams'."

"But nobody saw her. Mary Turnham declares Ann didn't come back there," said Bill Barker. "She says she seen her a-followin' you boys at a distance, clear into the woods. Abe, you'll just have to go along with us and show the way you went."

He turned abruptly and mounted his horse, and the others swung into their saddles. Tom Lincoln came out in a hurry and saddled his two horses. He mounted one, Abe the other, and the men and horses and the flaring torches rode out into the night woods.

"It'll be a fair mercy if they don't set the whole woods afire," murmured Sarah Lincoln, closing the door.

"Will the panthers eat Ann if they find her first?" asked Tilda, big-eyed, lip quivering.

"No, honey, but a panther is a mean varmint, and, well—we won't talk about it now. We'd best pray that little Ann is found, and soon."

With a sudden flash of understanding, Abe remembered the track of a small bare foot in the mud at the ford. The horses went down the deer trail and to the creek, and Abe dismounted quickly, before they would trample out any more prints, and hunted over the mud for them.

The boy was getting sicker and sicker at heart. Ann Roby was such a dear, sweet little thing, just a bit younger than he, and so pretty and neat and smart and lively. He could almost have wept, thinking of her out in the forest alone in the night, and he not there to protect her and keep her from being afraid. The voice of a wolf off in the distant hills came to him, lonesome and frightening. Worst of all was Abe's inner realization that, if he had been kinder, if he had let Ann come along on the expedition, she wouldn't now be lost in the dark. It was his own fault, whatever happened to her, and he'd have it on his conscience for the rest of his life.

There was nothing to do but range out through the woods and

along the creek bank where the low water made it possible to ride fairly easily, the horses' hoofs sucking in the mud. The moon came up, full and big, over the forest and put a patchy brightness on the ground. There was a thin, low-pitched murmuring of dry autumn leaves, not yet fallen from the trees, as an almost imperceptible, leaf-fragrant breeze moved them.

Along the creek Abe found more tracks and followed them until they turned into the woods and were quite lost. He stood undeterminedly in the moonlit shadows, uncertain what to do next. Light from the torches caught up with him and he stood tall, silhouetted against the glare. Then he heard a small, tired, frightened voice coming to him.

"Abe! Abe! Here I am!"

Ann Roby, her dress torn and full of burs and sticktights from the autumn woods, stumbled out of the darkness and flung herself upon Abe, who gathered her into his arms. He could feel her tears running through his shirt; their warmth made him feel unutterably tender and protecting.

"You're all right, Annie!" he said soothingly, smoothing her tangled curls. "Here she is!" he bellowed to the others, who came running. Absolem Roby removed his daughter from Abe's arms and took her into his own, and carried her down to the waiting horses.

"Daughter! Daughter!" he cried. "Are you all right? Whatever possessed you to run away like that? We been worried to death, fearin' for you! Your mammy's fair prostrate, thinkin' the panthers had got you!"

"I'm all right, only awful tired and hungry, Pa," Ann murmured. "I only wanted to see where Abe and the boys were going with that sled and the horse, so I tagged along behind, but down by the creek I lost them, and I got confused and didn't know which was the way back. Oh, I'm so hungry! I found a big old hollow tree and crawled into it, thinking maybe the varmints wouldn't see me there. I guess I was asleep and when I woke, there was the fire of your torches. I saw Abe standing there—oh, I'm so glad you found me, Abe!"

ALONG THE CREEK ABE FOUND MORE TRACKS AND FOLLOWED THEM UNTIL THEY
TURNED INTO THE WOODS AND WERE QUITE LOST.

"STAY AWAY!" HE SHOUTED TO THE PUPILS. "GO GET HELP! THERE'S A BEAR OR
SOMETHIN' IN THE SCHOOLHOUSE, AND THIS'N WON'T LET ME DOWN!"

CHAPTER THIRTEEN

THE HONEY and wax brought six dollars and fifty cents. Honey was seventy-five cents a gallon, and the old tree had held a record quantity. Tom went along to see that Abe didn't get skunked on the sale. Grudgingly, he permitted all the proceeds to go toward paying for another month of school, but there wasn't enough for John D., who didn't much care anyway. The problem of finding a way to go to school for another month after that, and another and another, as long as there was a teacher who would stick it out, had to wait for the future to solve. It was enough for young Abraham Lincoln that he had another month of school to look forward to.

One morning he and Tilda were walking down the road on the four-mile stretch to school. John D. was tagging along as far as the Crawfords', where he figured maybe Mrs. Crawford would have some leftover breakfast to give him. Abe and Tilda picked up Mary and Lucy Turnham and Bessie Oskins and Allen Brooner along the way. Allen Gentry usually caught up with them from farther back a piece. That crisp October morning, the talk was about the root doctor in town.

"I heard tell he's got a great big swamp lily root almost as big as a man, all carved up, like, and painted, so's it looks almost *like* a man, and he's got it hung up at the door of the house where he lives. They say he kin cure most anythin' with roots and yarbs," said Abe Lincoln.

"Kin he cure the ague?" asked Bessie Oskins, a fat, plain-looking girl with rope-colored braids and a splash of bacon grease down the

119

front of her coarse brown dress. "My paw's had the ague so bad he jest shakes and shakes, when it's on him. One day he was out huntin', and he started shakin' so bad he jest had to set down on to a stump and let the ague take him. He was sittin' there, shiverin' and jumpin', when a stranger man come up to him and they was passin' the time of day when a buck deer run right down the trail and never seen the men there. It jest stood there, and Paw wanted so bad to shoot, but he couldn't hold the gun steady. It jest wabbled and shook, and he put it down. He was near cryin', I reckon. So the stranger man, he up and shot, and got the buck deer, and my paw sure was beholden to him. He'd had sech a hard time shootin' any table meat since the ague took him, we've been livin' mostly on pone and salt pork. That buck deer sure come in handy, and he'll get a dollar-and-a-half for the hide, too, I reckon. You think the root doctor kin cure my paw?"

"Sure, he says he kin cure anythin', shakes and spavine and the janders and the bold-hives, and all such," asserted Allen Brooner. "He's a queer sort of feller, with big lookin' glasses to his eyes and a long beard, sort of dusty-like all the endurin' time, and he wears a real stylish suit of black broadcloth, no buckskins nor butternut jeans for him! I tell you, he's a great man. They say he'll teach others, too, how to cure with roots, and he gives a certif'cate at the end of three weeks of study, provin' you've learnt what he had to teach."

"What's it cost?" asked Jim Grigsby, who had joined the group at the last crossroad lane, along with four other Grigsby brothers and sisters, who employed their time with making faces at Abe and Tilda, wiggling fingers from ears and crossing their eyes. Tilda and Abe, who were used to Grigsby insults, studiously ignored their efforts. "I might even quit school," Jim Grigsby bragged, "and go in town and learn how to be a root doctor. I hear there's big money to it."

"I don't know how much it costs, but I sure don't aim to spend none of my money on it," sniffed Allen Gentry.

"What money *you* got to spend?" scoffed Jim. "Your paw ain't never let you have two bits of your own to rub together. 'Sides that, you ain't smart enough to learn how to be a root doctor nor anythin' else!"

"Who said I ain't smart enough!" screamed Allen. "And my paw is nigh the richest man around this county, and if I wanted money he'd give it to me—and send me to study in town, too, if I wanted!"

Allen doubled his fists and lit into Jim, who was a head taller than he. Jim promptly laid his books in the road and whaled into Allen. The two rolled energetically in the dust while the others stood about, jumping up and down in excitement.

The girls pretended to be frightened, and then their fright was genuine as Allen's nose suddenly spouted dark red blood which blossomed beautifully crimson on his white shirtfront.

"He's killed, he's killed!" bugled Lucy Turnham. "He's killed, he's killed, he's killed!"

"Oh, hush up, Lucy," said Abe in disgust at her idiocy. "He's only got the nosebleed. He ain't killed nor even bad hurt, though his maw ain't goin' to like the look of that good shirt. Come on, Allen, get up, and I'll wash you off."

"He ain't goin' to call me no dummy," Allen blubbered, feeling of his nose and becoming more alarmed at the sight of the blood than at any slight pain he was enduring.

"Well, forget it," went on Abe. "Fightin' ain't goin' to settle nothin', whether you're smart nor stupid. And if we don't git to makin' tracks down this here road, we'll be late and books'll be took up before we git there. And you know what old Turkey-cock Swaney'll do to us!"

The bright scarlet of Mr. Swaney's wattled neck was burgeoning brightly when the group from south on the road hove into sight. Allen's shirt was still a dismal thing, and Jim and Allen were full of dust.

"Well, well, come on, come on, don't take all day!" Mr. Swaney called. "Lateness is a sin!"

When the pupils were installed hastily on their seats, Turkey-cock Swaney took up the Bible to read the morning prayer, but he kept a long switch in the other hand, and when the pupils were supposed to be closing their eyes in prayer, he kept his open, and woe to the one who was caught with his eyes open, too, and doing something besides praying.

" 'And Jesus said'—Chris Olsen, close your eyes and fold your hands!—'blessed are the meek for they—', All right, David Turnham, come up here!"

David came, was briskly switched across the hands for inattention, returned to his seat, and James Swaney continued blandly with his reading from Scripture.

"Take out your books," ordered the teacher and opened his. Abe Lincoln's hand shot up bonily, far above the end of his sleeve.

"Well, Mr. Lincoln?"

"Mr. Swaney, did you hear about the panthers that tried to tear apart the schoolhouse over to Big Deer Lick last week? I heard Mr. Crawford tellin' my paw, and—"

"I don't want to hear about it now, Mr. Lincoln. Get to work on your spellin'!"

"But, Mr. Swaney, there's so many panthers around here, I thought you ought to know . . ."

"Well, tell it quick, and be done with it," said James Swaney, interested in spite of himself. "But make it short. Though I doubt me that you will," he sighed.

"Well," said Abe, delighted to have the floor. "A hunter done killed a young panther near this here schoolhouse and left the carcass there for his boy to carry home. A little while after books was taken up, the teacher and pupils heard a most awful scream outside! They looked out quick and saw the old mother-panther boundin' along, straight toward the schoolhouse, till she spied her dead young one!" Abe paused for effect and then continued.

"Well, the teacher, he slammed the door and shoved a bench across it and closed the window. They could hear the awful noises out there that the old she-cat was makin' when she'd discovered her young one was dead, and then she took a long look at the schoolhouse and ran straight toward it and commenced to run around it and around it, yowlin' with each bound, three or four times. Then what should she do but leap clean up on to the roof clapboards and parade around up there, tryin' to find a way to get in and tearin' at the roof and sniffin' down the chimney and yowlin', so her voice come down that chimney piece right to where the teacher and the pupils was hidin' in fear of their lives! Pretty soon, what did they hear but *another* panther screamin', and here come the pappy-panther. They both got up on to the roof again, screamin' and clawin' at the clapboards, till the teacher and the pupils was well-nigh scared to death."

Everyone was hanging upon his words. Mr. Swaney looked a little sick. It was easy to see that he was picturing himself in a like situation and not relishing the notion.

"By and by," Abe continued, "some men cuttin' timber heard the racket and they come runnin' with their dogs and guns. Well, the men shot both the panthers off that there schoolhouse roof, and that was the end of them. I hear the teacher vows he's goin' to quit, come next week, and go back to Pennsylvania. He calculates panthers is too much to ask a teacher to take on. The young ones he tries to teach is bad enough!"

Abe sat down, grinning, while the boys and girls exclaimed over the tale, and James Swaney sat back in his chair, more shaken than he would have admitted. The story left him with a cold feeling in his stomach, and it was with difficulty that he got the blab-school started on its spelling.

But the next morning, the story of the panthers still fresh in their minds and the topic of conversation and argument on the long walk to school, the first pupils, among whom were Abe Lincoln, and Tilda Johnston, came upon an astounding sight.

James Swaney, his neck and face redder than ever, was up in a small tree near the school. A big black bear was pacing below.

"Stay away!" he shouted to the pupils. "Go get help! There's a bear or somethin' in the schoolhouse, and this'n won't let me down! Hurry!"

Abe sprinted down the road to the Turnhams and came back with the judge and his rifle, as well as Chris Olsen's father and Zeb Enlow, all armed. It was a matter of small incident to dispatch the bear. James Swaney shakily slid down from his perch in the sassafras tree, losing a little skin in the process. He could hardly talk for his nervousness and excitement.

"There's another in the schoolhouse," he kept saying, over and over. "It's tearin' around in there, turnin' over benches and whatever and raisin' Old Ned. It's a bear or maybe could be a panther! Listen!"

There was, indeed, something in the schoolhouse. It sounded like a full-grown bear or maybe two, or a panther, or maybe two or three of each.

Gingerly, Judge Turnham opened the door, and the other men stood ready with their rifles cocked. A black bear cub, about half-grown, appeared, puzzled, blinking in the light. The guns blazed.

Inside the log schoolhouse, the benches were overturned, and the contents of Mr. Swaney's desk were scattered over the puncheon floor.

"But how could a bear get into my schoolhouse?" James Swaney babbled, tremblingly righting his mistreated belongings. "The door was closed, latched on the outside. How could a bear get in?"

Judge Turnham inadvertently answered the puzzle just then by stepping on a loose floor puncheon, which tipped into the air and the judge lost his balance, skinned his ankle, and fell in a heap.

"Your bear must have got in that-a-way," said the judge grimly, getting up and nursing his ankle. "Likely your pupils threw some of their lunch under the schoolhouse, and the bears were foraging around for food and smelled it under there. And likely the cub pushed against the loose puncheon by accident, and it opened and he climbed up. Then it closed and trapped him there. I suggest you fix that puncheon, Swaney, before you get more than bear cubs in this here schoolhouse!" Judge Turnham stalked off, limping.

The wild life of Indiana was getting to be too much for James Swaney. Panthers on the roof of a compatriot's school not many miles away from Pigeon Creek, the danger of wolves in the woods roundabout, and now bears in his own schoolhouse! It was too much for a civilized man to endure. At the end of four months of teaching at the subscription school, Turkey-cock Swaney gathered up his few belongings and went away.

Perhaps the person who missed him most was Abraham Lincoln, who, now nearly fourteen, yearned with a tremendous and restless inward yearning for books to read and big things to puzzle his mind upon.

"You'll just have to find books roundabout," said Sarah Lincoln in desperation one day, when Abe was fuming and ranting about because he didn't have a thing that was new to read, and he had worn threadbare and thin-papered the few books Sarah had brought with her when she came.

"My best friend is the one who will find me a book I haven't ever read!" said Abe grumpily. "Only, seems I haven't got any friends!"

But there were plenty of friends for Abe Lincoln, and books, too, at least enough for a while. At the rate he devoured them, a few wouldn't last long.

"You like to read, don't you, Abe?" Josiah Crawford asked abruptly, watching the boy staring at the backs of the leather-bound books in the Crawford house, but not touching them because nobody had given him leave.

"Yes, sir," spoke up Abe, looking around into Josiah's level, stern eyes, which always seemed so cold and fierce and intolerant, yet masked but poorly one of the kindest natures in Spencer County.

"Well, as you can see, I've got some books," went on Josiah gruffly, "and I reckon that, now you're fourteen, you're old enough to be careful of them. You must be sure to take care, so's they don't get damaged, and don't let the young ones get hold. Otherwise, you can read all you want."

"Oh, can I really?" cried Abe, beaming, a great light in his face. "Mr. Crawford, I'll do anythin' you want done to pay for it—if you'll just let me get at them books!"

Josiah grinned wryly at the excited boy.

"No need to barter yourself away," he grunted. "You go ahead. Take home a book you want to read. And later, if I need some work done, I reckon you'll help me."

"I sure will!" promised Abe fervently, eyes alight.

It was hard, in this sudden beneficence, to decide which book to take first, but he finally settled on Parson Weems' *Life of Washington*.

Abe carried it home with him, buttoned into his jacket so he could feel it hard against his eager heart all the way. He hated to have to chop kindling when he reached there, but the job was waiting.

Tom Lincoln was in an unusually expansive mood. He saw the boy's eagerness, his loving hands fingering the book.

"Oh, set down and git at the readin', Son," he said suddenly. "I reckon Dennis or John D. can cut up that there kindlin' wood for your maw this time. But you got to make up for it tomorrow!" The glad look Abe shot him made Tom feel warm inside, somehow.

It was all Abe could do to break away from Parson Weems for supper.

Dennis remarked, "I reckon Abe don't know *what* he's eatin' when he's got his face in a book. Might as well feed him cow fodder and crab apples, *he* wouldn't know the difference!"

When Abe got up, not even hearing the witticism, and headed for the book, Dennis put out his leg and Abe sprawled headlong over it, knocking over a stool and upsetting the poker.

Dennis guffawed and Tom grinned and John D. yelped with joy. The girls giggled. But Sarah looked stern.

"That's enough, Dennis Hanks," she said crisply. "You got no call to torment the boy just because he's interested in a book. Wouldn't hurt you none to read a book now and then, seems like."

Abe picked himself up without a word and got his treasure. It was late when he finally quit because his eyes hurt. He took the book up into the loft with him so it wouldn't be played with by John D., and there was no telling what Dennis, a practical joker of the worst sort, might think up to do with it. Abe tucked the book into a special hiding place up under the eaves, where it would be safe, and went to sleep almost at once.

He woke early in the morning to the sound of rain beating on the clapboards above his head. There was a drip coming in on where he slept, and he moved over to get out of its way. He was about to go to sleep again, when a sudden thought burst like a running rabbit into his mind. He sat up in panic and groped for the book, the volume of George Washington's life.

His heart did a double flip-flop and then sank somewhere out of sight as his fingers closed around the pulpy, soggy cover of Josiah Crawford's precious book. Abe was almost afraid to draw it out of the hiding place; he was sick at heart at what he knew he was going to see.

Even in the dim light of the loft, the book looked awful. It looked even worse when he dragged himself down the ladder and made himself examine the stained and swollen pages. He slumped down at the table and put his face in his hands.

"What in the world's the trouble, Son?" asked Sarah worriedly, looking up from frying fat pork for breakfast. "What's happened?" She came over and laid her hand lovingly on the boy's bony shoulder and felt his despair. "Tell me."

"Oh, it's Mr. Crawford's book," Abe said hopelessly. "He was good enough to lend it to me, and now just look what I've done! Look!" He held up the mess, and Sarah winced. It did look bad. And there certainly was no money around right now to buy a book like that to replace it for Mr. Crawford.

"Well, it does look pretty terrible," she agreed, keeping her voice casual, though she knew what he was feeling and longed to sympathize. "But I reckon Josiah'll understand and find a way for you to pay for it."

"I guess," said Abe, without enthusiasm. It wasn't so much having to find a way to pay for the book, it was having spoiled it—having permitted the ruination of something which meant so much to him. It was wicked to hurt a book.

He made himself go down to the Crawfords' in the rain. He stood on one foot and then on the other, trying to find the right words.

Elizabeth Crawford looked at him, exasperated, from where she was energetically thumping the churn.

"Abe Lincoln, you are the worst plaguéd boy I ever saw!" she exclaimed. "What on earth's ailing you, anyway? Get it out, and don't just stand there hemming around and teetering from one foot to the other like a big old craney-crow down in the swamp. Speak up, boy, I won't bite you!"

"Mis Crawford," he began desperately, pulling the ruined book out of his jacket and thrusting it forward. "Look what I done to that book Mr. Crawford gave me the loan of!"

"Josiah," she called, after one shocked look at the book. "Come here a minute. Abe here's got something to show you."

Josiah Crawford looked sternly from under his black brows at the book held out to him and at the desperate face of the gangling boy.

Josiah scowled, but his words were surprisingly kind.

"Well, I reckon you didn't do it a-purpose, Abe," he said. "If you'll pull fodder for me for three days, I reckon that'll more than pay for the book. That suit you?"

"Suit me? Oh, Mr. Crawford, that'll suit me right down to the ground! I'll get started right away. I'll pull all the fodder you've got, if that'll pay for the book!"

"You've got no call to go out in this here rain and pull fodder and likely catch your death," decreed Elizabeth. "You go on home and put that book nigh to the fire so's the pages can somewhat dry out, and keep separating them so they don't stick, and when the rain's over, you come back and work. Meanwhile, you help me get this butter out and I'll give you a piece of light bread, fresh out of the oven. And there's naught finer to eat than new butter on hot white bread, nor anything better to put heart back into a man!"

When Abe went home, he did as he was told. The book dried out pretty well, but it was undeniably spoiled in appearance. He worked out his three days pulling fodder as hard as three men could work, and when he finished the field, Josiah Crawford said:

"Well, Abe, seems like you more than paid for that book. I've read it lots of times and have no more use for it; it's yours, boy. You more than paid me for it!"

There were other books to read when Abe finished Parson Weems. With Sarah Lincoln's approval warm upon him, Tom Lincoln tolerated Abe's bookishness as long his son did his work. The work had to be done, there was no getting around it, and the boy couldn't be allowed to lie around all day reading, just because he wanted to. Tom often laughed at the undeniable fact that, if Abe had a book waiting for him, he sailed through a job of work like a house afire. He felled trees in the forest with the sound of a whole lumber gang at work, and he read while he ate his lunch out there among the trees and wild creatures. He snaked logs and whipsawed planks and split rails and laid up fences—and spouted pieces he'd memorized. When the day's work was over, he ate with a book propped up at his plate, then read until his eyes wore out at night. His father let him do it. This was better than Dennis's vices, Tom figured. Abe would have a better education than he did, and likely he'd get farther in life, though Tom couldn't see how some of that stuff would help a man get on in the world. Fairy stories like the *Arabian Nights* and *Aesop's Fables*, and that nonsense which Judge Pitcher loaned him, something about a *Midsummer Night's Dream*, that had donkeys and fairies and play-actors in it, which Abe was going around reciting, and *Julius Caesar*, too—Tom couldn't see any good to them. But he let his son read, provided the work was done.

One day when Abe was helping his father in the back field, George Carter rode up to talk to Tom Lincoln and hauled out a paper, which Tom pretended to read. He often did this; it saved him the embarrassment of admitting that he couldn't read much of anything. He turned the paper around, squinting at it. The document looked sort of legal and important, and George Carter told him to hurry up and sign his name, since this was the deed to the ten acres which Tom had decided last week to sell to Carter. Tom figured he'd just have to take Carter's word for what was on the paper.

"Well, come to the house," sighed Tom, hoping the paper was all fair and square because George Carter assured him it was. "I'll sharpen up a quill and see if we got any ink left. Seems like Abe made some out of oak galls last week and he might not have used it all. Plaguéd boy, all the time writin' and readin'," he blustered, to make conversation.

Sarah was in the house. She didn't like him, rat-faced George Carter, and she didn't like the legal look to the paper in Tom's hand, but he wouldn't let her see it.

She stepped to the door and waved her apron twice to Abe out in the far field, a signal they had between them. Abe saw it and came on the lope. He was just barely out of breath when he ambled casually through the open doorway as his father was dipping the freshly sharpened goose quill into the pot of oak-gall ink.

"What're you doin', Paw?" Abe asked in a noncommittal voice, winking over at Sarah, who was mightily relieved to see him.

"I'm a-signin' my name, if you must know," grunted Tom testily, bending over the paper.

"What on, Paw?" Abe tried to get a squint at the document.

"Oh, go ahead and read it, boy," sighed Tom, leaning back. "You might as well, since you're a-bound to anyway. Never saw such a inquisitive boy as that son of mine," he said apologetically to George Carter, who was backing unobtrusively toward the door.

Abe looked up, frowning. He gazed sternly at Carter, who by then was halfway out of the door.

"Paw," Abe said sharply, thrusting a thumb contemptuously at the paper, "if you sign that there paper, you're signin' away your rights to *this whole farm*. That document says you're sellin' the entire farm, not just ten acres!"

With a roar, Tom leaped to his feet, his face flaming and fists clenching, but George Carter had fled to the hitching rail and was hastily mounting his horse.

"You better go!" Tom yelled after him. "My boy kin read and thankful I am that he kin, savin' his whole family from losin' their farm! You're a blasted scoundrel, Carter, and don't you dast set foot on this here land again, or I'll take you apart and scatter your remainders to the buzzards!"

Tom turned to Abe.

"Son," he said, "don't you never pay no mind to what I say about you takin' time to read. I don't really mean it. You got to get your work done, like all of us got to, but you go ahead and study all you kin get hold of. If you hadn't of known how to read so well, and didn't know a morsel of law you've learnt off Judge Pitcher, likely, I'd-a signed away everythin' we got, all on account of my own endurin' ignorance!"

Tom turned abruptly toward the fire. Abe laid his hand on his father's bent shoulder for a moment, before he went out again to the field.

CHAPTER FOURTEEN

"Paw, the Griffys are back again," announced Abe one day in April when the lady's-slippers were blooming golden in the woods. "Allen Gentry said the Griffys are buildin' huts, like, around the big spring over on the Wentworths' land, and old man Wentworth and his brother ain't even fixin' to throw 'em off."

"Many folk with 'em this year?" asked Tom curiously. The Griffys were a tribe of people, almost all connected by blood ties, who lived as a clan, apart from other folk. They were not exactly like gipsies, but they did take their few belongings and travel in covered wagons down south somewhere for the winter. Then they migrated back to Indiana for the spring and summer and the long, gentle autumn.

Several weeks after the Griffys had thrown up their rude huts around the Wentworths' spring, Casway and Issachar Griffy came to the Lincoln farm and knocked on the cabin door.

Sarah Lincoln looked out.

"Griffys," she thought, "they must want something. They always want something."

"Good morning, gentlemen," she said pleasantly, yet keeping her eyes warily upon them every moment. Take your eyes off a Griffy, and something always turned up missing.

"Mornin', Mis Lincoln," Issachar drawled gravely, removing his ancient, green-stained beaver hat from his tangled gray hair. "Is Mr. Tom at home?"

"He's out in the field," said Sarah, wishing they would go away.

131

"Thank-e, ma'am," said Issachar and Casway solemnly together, bowing, and they hurried out to see Tom.

"Mr. Tom," began Issachar, with no more ado. "You got some cut money, small silver change for a dollar? I got a whole, good, sound, silver dollar, Mexican silver, that I'll give you for enough change in bits and quarters to make it up."

"Think ye silver that size would melt up in a ladle with lead?" asked Casway cautiously.

A warning clicked in Tom Lincoln's brain. Counterfeiters! The Griffys had taken to putting out false money.

"Well, I must say!" he exclaimed reprovingly, drawing back. "I never thought you Griffys would stoop to makin' worthless coin! Times is bad and money scarce, but—counterfeitin'! That's cheatin' the U.S. government! I'd be ashamed, if I were you. Don't you git me mixed up in any such a shady business. I'll turn you in to the sheriff, that I will!"

Casway and Issachar Griffy fell back in alarm. Their pale eyes stood out, their mouths gaped a moment and their pasty faces looked even more drained of color than usually.

"Oh, no, Mr. Tom, we ain't thinkin' of no such a thing!" cried Casway, his hands shaking. "We got too much trouble now to ask for anythin' like that!"

"What kind of trouble?"

"*Witches!*" whispered Issachar, leaning forward to utter the dread word, his pale eyes out on stalks again. He glanced around to make sure no one heard. Abe was down at the far end of the field, guiding the bull-tongue plow.

"Witches! What on earth you talkin' about?" cried Tom Lincoln impatiently. The men were clean crazy. "They ain't no witches nowadays. What you talkin' about?"

"Witches. One witch, leastways," stated Issachar positively and Casway nodded vigorously, his lips pressed tightly together. "We know. We got proof. And now we want to melt down some silver and lead to make a silver bullet so's we kin shoot the witch woman that's abotherin' of us. We cain't stand it no longer!"

This was getting more and more complicated to Tom. He perched

132

on the hickory rail fence and invited his visitors to join him.

"Set down, gentlemen," he said patiently. "Start at the beginnin' and talk slow, one at a time, so I'll git it straight."

The two looked cautiously around again.

"I wouldn't want anyone to know this but you, Mr. Tom," began Issachar reluctantly. "We kep' it a secret, up to now, but seein' as how you think we aim to make counterfeit money out of melted-down lead and silver, I reckon we got to tell you the truth."

"It better *be*," warned Tom.

"Well," began Issachar, "when we was down in Tennessee this past winter, we begun to have a whole passel of troubles. There was an old woman lived near by; she was the terror of the countryside. She lived all alone in a little old hut in the woods, with no man to do for her, yet she always had plenty to eat, seemed like. She had a little field of corn that always was cultivated and tooken care of, yet no one ever saw nobody doin' a lick of work around the place. Got so folk said she was a witch.

"You should of seen her. She went ridin' horseback without a saddle, astride like a man, her skirts up to her knees. She always rode the wildest, most unbroken horses around and about, and law, how she could fight! She could knock down the biggest man in the village. She had a way with her! She could stand there innocent-like, smilin' a little—and without her teeth it were a big soft smile that nigh brought her nose and chin together—and when a man came near, lo and behold, the old witchwoman mere put out her hand, and next thing you saw, that man was lyin' on the ground, flatter'n a door, and the old witchwoman was still a-smilin' there, ca'm as you please."

"It's my turn now," put in Casway pointedly, and Issachar kept quiet. "Well," went on Casway, "we done had cows down in Tennessee, four of them, and they was good milkers. But by and by we could only get milk from two at a time; the other two was always dry. The old witchwoman, she never kept no cows, but she always had plenty milk and cream and butter, had it to sell in town. My wife, she decided she'd find out what was goin' on. One mornin' she went up to the old witchwoman's house, unbeknownst to her, and hid near by to watch. Well, first thing she seen was the witch doin' somethin' to a towel that was hangin' in a window.

"First she took a pin and stuck it in the towel and said, 'I name ye Bossy!' which was the name of one of our own cows. Then she took hold of the fringe of the towel and commenced to pull it like she were milkin' a cow. When she had finished, she took another pin and said, 'I name ye Peidy!' which was the name of Cousin Bazalul Griffy's cow. She went through the same business again, while my wife, watchin', felt cold chills run over her, at seein' such witchcraft. When my wife got back home, lo and behold, Peidy and Bossy was already milked dry as a bone!

"We didn't know what-all to do," went on Casway, relishing the tale. "At night the old witch took the form of a black cat. We never knew where we'd find that pesky cat, and we never could lay hands on her."

"Finally," broke in Issachar, "Camadovas Coy, one of the old folk we got with us, he seen the cat run into his room. He got the shake-ax, and when the cat run out, he slashed down but only cut off the tip of one of its ears. Next mornin' one of of our women went over to call on the old woman and found her lyin' in bed with a bandage over her head.

"After that, whenever we seen the black cat, its right ear was cropped, and the old woman kept her cap down so's her right ear wouldn't show.

"Well, it's a sad and turrible story," continued Issachar gustily. "When we come north we brought them four cows along, thinkin' to get away from the old witchwoman's antickin' around, but just a few days ago, when Judah and Siloam was huntin' in the woods, what should they see but that selfsame crop-eared black cat!

"The old witchwoman's after us agin. And them cows that'd give good milk, all four of 'em, now is the same as they was down in Tennessee. Besides, we got a lot of sickness in our camp, and I lay it all to the witchwoman. Now, if we was to make us a silver bullet and shoot that there black cat, we'd be a-killin' that witch and our troubles'll be over. Now, *will* you give the change for this dollar, Mr. Tom?"

Tom Lincoln didn't know whether to laugh or to take them as seriously as they took themselves. It sounded odd, but it could be true—or could it?

"Well," he said, "let's go in the house and see what I got in the till."

CHAPTER FIFTEEN

It was in 1824, when he was fifteen, that Abraham Lincoln first
heard of the strange folk who were living not far from where he
was growing up into a lanky, thoughtful, impatient boy who was
violently eager for new things, new lands, new adventures, new
books. He grew desperate at times with the futility of bucking in-
difference or of the hope of ever getting away from the backwoods
and finding a proper education. He loved the woods, and he loved
Indiana, but he would willingly leave both for a chance at what he
wanted.

Perhaps, up until that time, it had never occurred to him that
everyone in southern Indiana was not like his family, his community
—varying from the worthy Crawfords, Robys, Gentrys, Turnhams
and Joneses, and fine folk like the Pitchers and Grahams, to the
shiftless Grigsbys, Oskinses and Lincolns. According to their several
degrees of education or lack of it, these people believed practically
the same things, went to church, were frequently of the Baptist per-
suasion, worked hard, ate about the same foods and wore about the
same kinds of garments. But some fifty miles away there was a community the like of which Abe had never suspected, a way of life
foreign to Indiana.

Josiah Crawford was visiting one evening and Absolem Roby was
there, too, when the subject came up for comment.

"Have you heard tell of them queer, Germanish folk over on the
Wabash?" Tom asked, making conversation. "That George Rapp
who's their king, or High Priest, or some such title, must be crazy

in the head, and that's my opinion!" he said firmly, as if that was all anyone needed to know of George Rapp and his ways.

"Well, it's a different way of living, at any rate," commented Josiah fairly, watching Abe where he was immersed in reading the *Autobiography of Benjamin Franklin* which he, Crawford, had just brought him. "From what I hear, they all work together for the good of all, which isn't such a bad idea. I was over there at Harmony on business a few months ago, and it was all mighty strange, I tell you!"

Abe looked up, interested, and listened closely.

"Every soul there was wakened between five and six in the morning by a band of music playing flutes and horns and drums, and such. It was something new to me, let me tell you! Nobody ever hailed *me* out of bed with a drum or flute!" Crawford laughed, remembering. "All day long the people do the work allotted to them, and the church bells time them. There are three bells in that church tower, and when they ring, you can hear them far up and down the river and out in the woods.

"At six o'clock at night, the bells ring to tell the Harmony people to stop work. They eat and sleep in community houses. Nobody owns anything; they own everything together, one and all alike. And do you know what, gentlemen?" asked Josiah Crawford quizzically. Abe lifted his head again. Dennis and Tom and Absolem Roby listened. Sarah put down her sewing, and Elizabeth hushed her baby, and Tilda, over in a dark corner, held tighter to the hand of Squire Hall, who had come sparking her.

"That fellow, Rapp," went on Crawford, "won't let any of his people wed! If any married couples join the group, they must dissolve the marriage, or at least live separately, the men in one house, the women in another. That's why the place is sure to die out. Old Rapp must be crazy, forbidding marriage. No way to build a civilization without new life coming in to perpetuate it!"

He leaned back and laughed again, a little, and the others joined in a great guffaw, thinking of the poor deluded Germanish people, the Rappites, over in Rapp's town of Harmony, with all their fine church bells and the music that woke them up in the morning, and all such, and no wives or husbands or children! It was laughable, it was that! And all so close to the good, sensible people of Pigeon Creek and Rockport.

"Did you hear about the big granary they got over there?" put in Absolem Roby. Abe listened, eyes on the book but not seeing the print. "Well, old George Rapp—Father Rapp, they call him—he wanted the biggest granary he could get built, so his whole community could go inside in case the Indians attacked, but he couldn't get his people interested. The old man ranted around, and then he had an idea. He sent down to the Mississippi by keelboat to get a couple of the big stone footprints he'd heard were down on the Indian rocks and he had slabs brought up by night and put into his garden, right by the door, set in the turf like as if they grew there.

"Then old Father Rapp called his people in a hurry next morning and said the Angel Gabriel had appeared before him and told him to get that there granary-fort built up right away, and he pointed to where Gabriel himself had done left his footprints, and the people saw them and like to fell down in a fit, they was so scared. The sight of them stone footprints sure made them work fast! They lit in and got that granary built for the old man before you could say scat. I saw it, too. Biggest buildin' this side of the Alleghenies, I make no doubt. All made of brick and ten times as big as this cabin, or more."

"But have you heard this?" put in Josiah. "I got it from Judge Pitcher down in Rockport, so I guess it's true. They say Rapp's up and sold his town, and they're all a-going back to Pennsylvania. He's sold it to fellow, name of Owen, from way off in Scotland. Why a Scot would come all the way to Indiana to buy land is beyond me, but them foreigners is unpredictable. And listen to what price he's paying—one hundred and fifty thousand dollars!"

There was a concerted gasp around the room. Dennis laughed shortly.

"Hah, I could buy me the hull state of Indiany, with Illinois throwed in, for half that amount!"

"A hundred and fifty thousand dollars!" exclaimed Sarah Lincoln, passing the bowl of sweet potatoes and knives to the guests so they could slice and eat their own. "I do hope this Scotsman knows what he's about!"

Abe's mind was racing. He was bound and determined to go over to the town of Harmony and have a look at the giant footprints in stone and the big granary, and listen to the bells, and see what he could see.

But months went by, and Abe had no chance. The Rappite community broke up. New people, sent by Robert Owen to populate his dream town, his ideal community, a city governed by reason, poured in. They came in flatboats down the Ohio and overland through the woods to the town renamed New Harmony.

In many places Owen and his leaders had contacted some of the brilliant minds of the period and induced them to come to New Harmony, to bring libraries and scientific collections, to bring themselves to build a little Arcady of culture in the wilderness of the Wabash valley.

It was in November, 1825, after an early, severe cold spell, that word came up from Rockport that a most extraordinary boatload of people was marooned in the ice up the river, a day's journey below Pittsburgh.

"Let me tell you," exclaimed Judge Pitcher in excitement to young Abe, who was browsing in his library again. "That's the most amazing boatload to set out on any river, in this country or any other! They've got some of the best minds of the times—there're teachers, some of them French, and artists and scientists—Thomas Say who went with Major Long to explore the Rocky Mountains, and Alexander LeSueur, a Frenchman, who has been all the way to the South Sea and even visited Australia! Imagine a man like LeSueur coming down the Ohio to live at New Harmony! And there's William Maclure, a wealthy geologist, and so many more. They are all aboard a big keelboat, but it's got stuck in the ice up near Beaver, Pennsylvania. I hear they sent about five tons of books and paintings and scientific instruments by sea around to New Orleans, and they'll come by steamboat up to New Harmony. Imagine, Abe, five tons of books!"

The thought was overpowering. It was inconceivable. Abe was

fascinated; he was in a daze of fine dreams in which he figured largely in connection with an endless number of new books.

"They've even got a pianoforte aboard that keelboat!" went on Judge Pitcher. "And now they're all fastened in tight in the ice. The river surely froze over early this year."

It was the wrong time of year to try a trip like that, everyone agreed, though in an ordinary year it would have been all right. The travelers had originally intended sailing by steamboat, but the river was too low for a steamboat to get through, so they took a keelboat, which would float on a heavy dew. Everything would have been fine if that unexpected zero cold hadn't caught them.

Abe worried about the books. He hoped nothing would happen to the ship that was taking the five tons of them by sea to New Orleans; hoped the steamboat bringing them up the Mississippi, the Ohio and the Wabash wouldn't blow up or be snagged or sunk. By the time Judge Pitcher had told him about the books and their hand-colored plates, he could hardly contain himself. They were the answer to his dreams and his prayers. If he had to stay in the backwoods and couldn't go to college in the East, then the college and the books at last were coming to him. Abe's whole inner being and mind burned more and more in impatience to get over to New Harmony when those wonders arrived—and see, and know, and understand. The key to all his questioning, his whole future, he felt, lay there.

For weeks the unseasonable cold locked the keelboat to the shore. Then there came a rise in the Allegheny River, whose ice broke and shoved toward the Ohio, meeting that impenetrable body of water. It thereupon backed up into the Monongahela, until great frozen mountains were violently heaped and shoved about. When the pack in the Ohio finally gave way at Pittsburgh, the Allegheny and the Monongahela burst loose. Great wedges, massive blocks of new and old ice, were shoving and grinding and moving at last, rumbling and crashing like cannon—the Ohio was open!

No boat could have survived the crush as the river broke up and the floes moved madly downstream, but the Boatload of Knowledge was out of the channel, tied against and frozen to the shore. This ice there was still immobile, until men broke out a channel to the open water, and the craft was on its way. At five miles an hour on the tumbling river, the Boatload of Knowledge swept toward its goal.

With the coming of geology, botany, chemistry, natural history, to New Harmony, the community had introduced a startling, fresh thought into the education of the young. Elsewhere, in most of the country, the sciences were still looked upon with considerable suspicion and distrust. They were actually banned by many a town which felt that these were forbidden fields.

Thomas Lincoln was sarcastic about New Harmony. He put a damper upon Abe's enthusiasm, so the boy simply kept it bottled up until he could talk it out with Judge Pitcher or Josiah Crawford.

"Oh, it won't last!" Tom Lincoln sneered one day. "It can't. There's nothin' right nor natural about it. All this education is just a-goin' to make the young folk discontent, and it'll unsettle their minds for work. Studyin' and readin' and talkin'—it'll cause brain fever, it's bound to. I hear tell they even favor higher education for females, and that'll be the ruination of 'em, I make no doubt."

Josiah Crawford put in, "They say they want first of all happiness for everyone." He smiled his wry smile.

Tom snorted. Words failed him. Happiness!

"They believe men and women are equal, and it doesn't matter if they're rich or poor, they're equal."

Tom snorted again.

"They say they want freedom of speech and freedom of education—they're startin' a school for young ones that're still so young they're hardly out of the cradle and a trade school and free schools for everyone as wants an education. There's a free library, too; anyone can go and borrow books there; and the females are startin' up a club where they study and give orations! Not only that, but they say they all got to be kind to everyone, not even whippin' the young ones when they disobey!" Here Tom laughed. "And they preach that folk must acquire knowledge to be happy and live right. But they don't hold with religion, and that'll be the ruination of the town, I make no doubt. Nobody can live long without religion. Education is all right, but you got to have the love of God in your heart and faith in His word if you want to live now and in the hereafter."

"Paw," Abe burst out, his eyes shining, choosing the worst possible time to broach the subject. "Paw, could I go to that there
free school over to New Harmony?"

If Abe had handed him a live rattlesnake, Tom Lincoln would
scarcely have been more startled, amazed, or taken aback—nor
more genuinely angry than he was at his son's request. He couldn't
speak for a moment. His face turned red-purple and his neck
cords stood out. Abe felt like running, but he stood where he was.
He was taller than his father, and he was at least as strong as he,
if not more so. He wasn't afraid of him, physically, but he did
hate a scene. And there was a scene coming up, as sure as anything,
rising like a tornado cloud on the horizon.

"Well!" exploded Tom Lincoln, taking a step forward as if he
would seize his son in his two bare hands and tear him apart, but,
aware of that young man's stature, his hands dropped. "Well! I
never thought I'd live to see the day when I'd hear a son of mine
say a thing like that! You've been mighty foolish all your endurin'
life, Abraham Lincoln, and I've humored you in a whole lot of
things because your maw wanted it. I've let her have her way, but
this—this takes the rag off the bush! Of course you cain't go over
to that blasted school at New Harmony! Even if you had all the
fancy riggin' you'd need to attend, I wouldn't allow you to set
foot one step in the direction of that Godless place! Didn't you
hear Josiah say they don't believe in religion? They're a lawless,
wicked, sin-ridden bunch of hypocrites and liars, and followers of
the Fiend himself!" Tom paused for breath. "But this I'm tellin'
you, Abe Lincoln," he went on violently. "You're my son, and
what I say is law to you. Till you're of age, you got to obey me,
and if I catch you goin' to that evil town, or talkin' to ary of its
ringleaders, or gettin' hold of ary book from there, I'll break your
neck with my bare hands, so help me!"

Abe was pale and shaken. He felt sick. He was only a boy. He
was only sixteen, even if he was too big for his paw to whip and
was as big as a man. He might look like a man and work like a
man, but he was still a boy; he had the painful sensitivity of a boy,

a sensitivity yearning and groping for understanding and kindness. Sarah Lincoln gave him both. She was the saving grace of living here with a father who was steadily growing more intolerant of his son's actions and his growing up.

Abe had always tried to mind his father. He had done nothing, he knew, to warrant all this railing that he got, and the threats of punishment. It was like when he was young and asked a question and had been beaten for it, when he'd meant no harm. The thought of going to the New Harmony school and of seeing the wonderful library there—five tons of books, so tantalizingly close to Pigeon Creek, yet as remote as the moon because of Thomas Lincoln's pronouncement—hurt him with a positively physical pain and brought uncontrollable tears welling up. To keep them from showing, he muttered something unintelligible and stumbled from the house. He went out into the darkness of a chill, late-winter night, and walked and walked and walked. He beat a clenched fist into the calloused palm of the other hand, over and over, crying out:

"I've got to! I've got to! I've just got to find a way!" And he walked on and on, along the hard, rutty road leading toward Rockport, until he felt more calm.

It was late when he let himself into the cabin, leaving his muddy moccasins on the doorstep, to be cleaned up in the morning, and went up to the loft quietly. He avoided the squeaky rungs of the ladder and didn't waken anyone.

Only Sarah knew when he came in. She had stayed awake, waiting for him, praying that he would come, that Tom hadn't finally driven the boy off with his intolerance, hadn't sent him away to a wild life on the river or—somewhere. Abe was at an age when he could fly off at a tangent and be lost to her forever, unless his own deep, good sense controlled him. Sarah sighed and turned over and let sleep claim her, now that she knew that Abe's good sense had indeed prevailed and brought him home again.

CHAPTER SIXTEEN

"I HEAR TELL that Sis Crawford and Bill Barker are finally goin' to get hitched," remarked Dennis Hanks one day some weeks later. His wife, Elizabeth, was busy with the new baby.

"Why didn't they get married long ago?" she asked incuriously. "They been goin' together as long as I can recollect. Handsome as he is, I'm surprised he waited. It's a wonder to me he ain't been snatched up long since."

"Well, most of the single females round about sure tried." Dennis laughed, stretching out on the bed to rest while the womenfolk got supper on.

"What ever kept her back, anyway?" asked Tilda, whose own plans for marrying Squire Hall were coming on apace.

"Oh, Sis swore Billy drank too much!" Dennis answered with a snicker. "If that kept folk from marryin', a whole lot would go without husbands *or* wives! Look at me—you didn't pay no mind because I took a drink now and then, did you, Bess?"

"Elizabeth might have used better judgment," put in Tom Lincoln sternly. "I always say a drinkin' man don't make no good provider."

"You think you been a better provider 'cause you never touch a drop?" sneered Dennis, rolling over to look at Tom.

"Yes, I do," asserted Tom Lincoln. "At least I ain't been spongin' off my kinfolk like some people I could mention!" Then he turned, as Abe came in, after washing up outside. "Abe," said Tom, "now's as good a time as any, I guess, since the subject done come up. You know I don't hold with the use of spirits, don't you?"

Abe looked at his father, wondering what he was driving at.

"Yes, Paw, I know."

"Well," went on Tom, while Dennis watched quizzically, "I want you should promise me that you won't touch nary a drop till after you're twenty-one. Will you do that?"

"Well," said Abe slowly, chancing a grin at his father and casting a quick look at Dennis, who had tried more than once to get young Abe interested in strong drink, "I'd sure like to promise that, Paw, but I'm afraid it won't be any use. Too late."

"What you mean, too late?" bristled Tom Lincoln, his big hands working.

"Now don't go and get roused up, Paw," soothed Abe. "There's nothin' to get excited about. I mean that, even when I do get to be twenty-one, I don't aim to start drinkin', then or ever. I just don't like the taste of the stuff."

"You mean you already done tasted it?"

"Well, they've been at me for years to have a drink," admitted Abe, including Dennis Hanks and Squire Hall. "I knew you didn't favor drinkin', but I figured I'd save myself a whole lot of mental anguish if I found out early whether or not I'd like it. Because—" he paused, and went on in the manner of Judge Pitcher, whose delivery he admired, "because, if I did like it, then I could begin to get my mind made up to stay away from the stuff; but if it so happened I didn't like whiskey, think of the time and effort I'd save, not havin' to work on myself and gettin' strong-minded and sacrificial and all! See, Paw? Since I just naturally can't abide the taste, why, I don't have to bother to take a pledge, and I don't have a thing to worry about and neither do you, before I'm twenty-one, or after, all my life!"

Tom Lincoln just sat back and looked at his son.

"Well, Abe," he finally said, pulling at his lower lip to keep from laughing, because Tom, in spite of his quick temper, was easily tickled with a joke—but he didn't favor acting undignified when he was correcting his children. "Well, barrin' some of them words which I don't know the meanin' of—and it beats me where you ever learnt 'em—I reckon you got a good point there. You stick to it, Son, and I reckon Squire and Dennis here would of been a whole lot better off if they had did the same. Not to mention John D., who's already got into bad habits."

"He's jest butterin' up to you, Tom," sneered Dennis, "so's to get on your good side. Likely he's got into trouble somewhere and wants to put you in a good mood afore he tells—or afore somebody tattles on him, likely!"

"You shut up, Dennis Hanks!" snapped Tom. "If Abe's got into trouble, I'll lay it into him accordin' to the sin he done. But I won't have no one laughin' at him 'cause he won't touch the Demon Rum! Now, Abe, did you rightly get into some trouble?"

"Oh, I just wrote somethin', and the Grigsbys found it by accident and have took exception to it," said Abe glumly, but honestly. "That ain't why I said that about the drink, though. It's the truth."

"What-all did you write about the Grigsbys?" pried Tom. "I told you and told you that you'd git into trouble with all that book-learnin'. It just ain't natural. Writin' poetry and stories and suchlike, the way you do these days."

"Oh, I wrote about that silly business of the double-weddin' at Grigsbys and how certain folk played a prank and mixed up the brides and grooms on the weddin' night, and how roused up old Mis Grigsby was. It all came out all right and no harm was done, but you recollect that for a while she was madder than a jay bird after snakes.

"So I wrote a piece called the *Chronicles of Reuben* and just accidentally dropped it on the road near their house, and, although only Natty and Billy can read, I guess they managed between 'em to make out what-all it said. Anyway, they're layin' for me."

"How-come you know so much about that there weddin' business? You wasn't invited." Tom was having a hard time keeping from laughing again. The business of the mixed-up couples at the wedding had been one of the funniest things he'd ever heard, and from all he'd learned later, he had a good notion as to who had engineered the whole thing.

"Oh, I don't know," said Abe vaguely, looking into the fire noncommittally. "They'd no business not invitin' me. And they sure didn't favor what I wrote. *I* thought it was real good."

"You git on up to your bed," said Tom. "I've had all I can stand of you this night. And I trust to mercy them Grigsbys do lay for you and cut you down to size!"

"Oh, let the boy have his supper," put in Sarah sharply. "He hasn't done anything so awful!"

The Grigsbys did wait for Abe. They caught him alone as he was cutting rails out near the main road. As usual, the sound of his ax blows sounded as if several men were working, which made the Grigsby boys hesitate a mite before going in to get their enemy.

But young Natty crept ahead and saw it was only Abe, swinging away at a great rate and declaiming to himself from the inaugural address of Thomas Jefferson, like an orator at a Fourth of July burgoo.

"Hey, you, Abraham Lincoln, we're out to git you!" growled Aaron Grigsby. "We know who writ that piece about the weddin', and we take exception to it. Come on out and fight like a man!"

Abe swung the ax in a single vast, glittering arc, and the Grigsbys ducked.

"Don't you dast heave that there ax at us!" screamed Billy, looking out from behind a tree. "Fight fair!"

"Yeah, fight fair," echoed Reuben Junior.

"See that you do," said Abe briefly, temporarily letting Thomas Jefferson rest and putting his ax in a safe place. Then he put his head down and ran like a charging bull straight at Natty Grigsby, who of all the Grigsbys was usually his friend, and grappled him around the waist. Natty yelled, battering ineffectually the strong back of his opponent. Abe tossed him into the group of his brothers. Then they all came at him in a mass, all but Natty, and the fight was on.

Abe Lincoln was always a little bit amazed at how strong he was. The day he carried a whole chicken house from one side of the yard to the other for Josiah Crawford had surprised him as much as it had amazed the neighbors. The muscles in his arms and back were big and powerful, and it gave him a certain joy to use them, to feel them swell and expand and do what he told them to. Fighting was all very well in its way, and fun, but he usually felt he had the advantage of his opponent. Most young fellows in Spencer County by now had learned to let him alone. But here he had five against him—though he saw that Natty was out of it now, sitting up against a tree trunk and blubbering.

Even Abe's superior strength had met its match in the four Grigsbys, who also had been reared in the wilderness, had cut their teeth on man-sized jobs that built muscles. But they, too, one by one, got knocked down and landed, sore and bruised, on the resilient forest floor.

Aaron and Abe were the last to grapple. It looked pretty well matched, though Aaron was breathing heavily, and Abe had not even lost his breath. They were down on the ground, rolling and straining and grunting. Aaron was on top suddenly and was gouging for his opponent's eyes, when Abe caught him with his knees and bounced him off. Aaron landed hard, with a sickening exhalation as the breath was knocked out of him. He lay still, green and sick, fighting for breath.

Abe stood up, his hands on his lean hips.

"Well," he said evenly, "if you want to have another go of it, come on. I got all day."

The Grigsbys lay where they had fallen and glowered at him.

"We'll get you for this, Abe Lincoln!" threatened Reuben Junior.

"I make no doubt you will," said Abe smoothly. "Likely you'll lay for me with a knife or whatever, or shoot me in the back, or some other little nicety you'll think up. But before then, don't you forget that I've beat you up today and I'll do it again, singly or all together, whichever you want. And that goes double for you, Aaron Grigsby, if I catch you foolin' around my sister again!"

He went back to his work, ignoring the five, and they got up silently and went home, hating him, but they'd had enough—all

148

but Aaron, who was sweet on Sally Lincoln and was bound to have her, in spite of everything her cocky brother said or did.

Sally Lincoln had grown into a slender, quiet girl, not as tall as Abe, but as thin. Not beautiful by any stretch of the imagination, Sally was strangely attractive, with her deep-set, dark eyes and her sensitive mouth which could make her face look so old and solemn when it was in repose and could blossom into the loveliest of smiles, breaking around her eyes and over her face, transforming her into a charming girl with a bubbling laugh.

Sally had two moods. She was either quiet and sad, or alight with happiness, though the sadness often predominated, as it often did in Abe. She remembered her mother more than her brother did and thought of her often. She had grown fond of Sarah Johnston as a stepmother, but she never felt for her the strange, linking bond of attachment which lay between Sarah and Abe. His eyes could look into Sarah's and interlock in a curious combining of wills and spirit and love. Sally tolerated her stepmother—loved her more than she herself would ever admit—but she never forgot Nancy, her real mother, nor recovered from her deep-lying resentment that her father should so far forget his first wife as to take another, and, in so doing, supersede in the household the place his daughter had held. That was rub; that was the basic hurt.

Sally at twelve had felt capable of running the household for her menfolk, but he had brought another woman to do her job. It didn't always matter that Sarah was far more capable, as an older, experienced woman, that she brought understanding, love, a higher standard of living and a certain elegance in her fine furniture and her demand for a floor and whitewashed walls and other improvements, all of which Sally could never have insisted upon nor provided.

The young men in the neighborhood, from time to time, had tried to go sparking with Sally Lincoln, but with dignity and a kindly smile, she had not encouraged them. When Aaron Grigsby came calling, however, and carried her to meeting over at the church her father had helped build when it was organized, she began to think in terms of marrying Aaron. He was a heavy-set young man of fairly good habits, owned a farm over near his father's, down south a piece from her own home and the church. She was helping out at the Crawfords' that year and Aaron came there to court her, for which she was thankful; there was more privacy at the Crawfords' place than in her own crowded one-room house.

Abe looked with suspicion on any man who came with the notion of courting his sister. None of them was good enough, he asserted, especially a Grigsby. Sally would smile at that and rumple his hair and tell him he was a flatterer, and Abe would scowl and say he wasn't, that he meant every word of it. The fellow who wed Sally Lincoln would have to be mighty fine to take her away from him!

When Abe knew that it was going to be Aaron Grigsby, in spite of everything he could do, his dislike for Aaron increased, if that was possible. Sally was nineteen, and in the wilderness that was middling old. Girls married young in the woods. Look at Elizabeth Johnston, marrying Dennis Hanks when she was only fifteen, and the mother of three children already and another on the way.

Abe sometimes wondered when Dennis would get up enough gumption to build himself a house of his own for his growing family. Goodness only knew, the Lincoln house with its one room and loft was crowded to the rafters with all the kinfolk—Thomas and Sarah, Sally and Abe, Elizabeth and Dennis and their young ones, Sarah, John and Nancy; and Matilda and John D. Thank fortune, Abe felt, when Cousin John Hanks came up from Kentucky in 1820 to live near the Lincolns, he had had the independence to build himself a house of his own; but John Hanks was a sturdy, self-willed, determined man who refused to live with his kinfolk.

Now Sally was going to leave the crowded household for a place of her own. Her father, however, would likely ask Aaron and Sally to live there with him—he had a patriarchal streak which made him feel that all his kin should be under one roof, even though

"HEY, YOU, ABRAHAM LINCOLN, WE'RE OUT TO GIT YOU!" GROWLED AARON
GRIGSBY. "WE KNOW WHO WRIT THAT PIECE ABOUT·THE WEDDIN'...."

THE MEN . . . DASHED WITH ABE TO THE SMALL ROWBOAT. THEY PILED IN AWK-
WARDLY, ALMOST SWAMPING THE CRAFT.

he never bothered to make that roof stretch widely enough to give all of them a degree of comfort. But Aaron, Sally knew, already had a house built, a house with two rooms and a dogtrot between, a more elegant arrangement than Sally had ever lived in before.

In spite of her brother's objections, Sally Lincoln was married to Aaron Grigsby on August 2, 1826, in the Pigeon Baptist Church.

With Sally gone, the house seemed strangely empty to Abe. It was full enough, goodness only knew, but some of its life which had been part of his own life since he could remember anything at all had gone out of it.

It was getting tougher, too, to live with Tom Lincoln, and Abe decided desperately that he would have to get away, if only for a little while. The chance came when he was at the mill, getting a grist ground, and James Taylor asked him if he would come and hire out to him on his farm for the rest of the growing season and the harvest. If he was satisfactory, then he'd have a job waiting in the spring.

It would be work, but there was plenty of that at home. And maybe if Abe wasn't there to do it, Dennis would do more, and maybe John D. would buckle down, especially with Tom Lincoln to drive him. Abe accepted the job. His pay of ten cents a day would come in handy to his father.

The job was downright hard labor, but Abe seemed to thrive on it, and on Mrs. Taylor's cooking, for he lived with his employer. His muscles were tough and he could manhandle logs and split wood for fence rails and plow and cultivate and butcher—anything James Taylor thought up for him to do, and he thought of plenty so that his hired hand would earn his ten cents. Abe proved so satisfactory, and Taylor got so much work done for a meager outlay of cash, that he kept the boy on after the harvest was in and the butchering over. Abe stayed there all winter and was handy when spring came and it was time to plow and plant.

The nearness of the Ohio River, however, made up for a whole lot. Taylor's land rose from the river shores. The width and beauty

of the Ohio had always fascinated the boy. The sight of a steamboat, the sound of its bells ringing and the whistle blowing for a
landing, the wonderful, exciting sound of steam, and the shouts
of the deck crew, made him long, with a desperate and intense
longing, to ride the river. He would choose a steamboat going to
New Orleans—for as long as he was wishing he might as well make
it good—but almost any kind of boat would do, if it was just
going somewhere. The river called with a most siren voice, and
the smell and sight and sound of the river became part of his life.
It was all the more so when James Taylor, raising his pay to
thirty-seven cents a day, put the boy to running the little ferry
he operated at the mouth of Anderson Creek. The ferry never
crossed the Ohio, but just went back and forth over the creek.
The river, however, was only a few yards away. It was always
near by, and Abe could dream of where he would go if he had
a chance and didn't always have to pole the ferry back and forth,
like a bead on a string, on the muddy little creek.

While Abe was cultivating or plowing in Taylor's rich bottomland cornfield, alert for a ring of the ferry bell to notify him that
someone was wanting to cross the creek, he was always aware of
the big water sparkling in the sun—water that never stayed in
one place, for rivers always went somewhere. He could see the
low hills of Kentucky beyond the bottoms on the other side, could
see steamboats moving grandly past, and flatboats and keelboats
and rafts and rowboats, all going somewhere with the busy river.

The very earth he turned over had a different smell from the
earth in the Lincoln fields, back on the uplands; the soil was rich
and dark from deposits left by many an Ohio River flood, dropped
when the water went down, year after year. That earth had,
somehow, taken into itself the odors of the river, and the aroma
grew stronger down on the bank where the willows grew.

Willows had a special smell, too. Their leaves on a summer day
had a rivery scent, and the curled, crisped, dried leaves of many
generations of willows, lying on the ground beneath the trees,
gave off a certain rank perfume which was always to be connected in Abe's mind with the character of rivers. All night in the

willows, hundreds of velvety black damsel flies roosted in the dewy leaves. They were still there when Abe came down to start work. Sunup would warm them and dry their thin, black silk wings. All day long in the willows the song sparrows caroled, oblivious to the heat. There was a mockingbird that performed its amazing repertory in a sycamore on the river-bank, and buzzards soared against a blazing summer sky.

When he was resting, or when he thought he wouldn't be missed, Abe went down to the creek and sat in a boat he had built, down in the shade of the willows and maples and sycamores. He would wish dreamily that he might untie the rope that fastened his homemade craft to a tree root and take the oars and paddle down the creek and out into the current of the big river, and go with it . . . somewhere, anywhere.

Sometimes he sat so long and so quietly in the boat, thinking, or else reading and rereading an old newspaper from Vincennes which he had hidden under the seat, that the birds and animals forgot he was there. The crayfish would come inching out of their mud chimneys on the shore, and sometimes a water snake slid along through the mud, leaving a sinuous trail as it moved into the water, in search of fish. Turtles came out on a driftwood log to sun themselves. The song sparrows peeped at him, and a cinnamon-colored wren flitted along, in and out of the exposed roots of the willows and sycamores where the water had chewed away the earth, and scolded at him when she came full upon him watching her.

The warmth, the smells from the water and mud and willow leaves, and the sounds of birds and the zizzing of dragonflies and all the other insect sounds of the hot Indiana summer, punctuated by the biting and buzzing of extra large Ohio River mosquitoes, were part of Abe's brief interludes along the creek.

Then the ferry bell would jangle noisily, and he'd have to get to his business, or James Taylor would roar at him from up in the field, demanding that he get back to work or he wouldn't eat, come night. And that would end the pleasant contemplation of laziness along the creek.

153

Abe often wished he could run a real ferryboat across the river and back, but the Dill brothers had the ferry franchise there on the Ohio. Still, occasions arose when Abe Lincoln had business on the river. There were no steamboat landings along here, but frequently someone aboard a steamboat wanted to come ashore at this point, or someone from Rockport or Newburgh or Boonville wanted to get aboard a boat that was pausing obligingly but impatiently in midstream. Abe usually got paid a quarter or so for doing this transfer work. Sometimes a passenger forgot to pay him anything, but it didn't really matter because he was doing it on James Taylor's time anyway.

One hot summer day when the stagecoach came rumbling along the river road, Abe hurried to get the ferry ready for it to cross. The coach halted, however, and two disheveled men leaped out, coattails flying, baggage in hand. One man hastily paid the stage driver and shouted at the top of his voice to a steamboat, the *Caroline*, which was approaching, bound downstream.

"Hey! Hey!" the man hallooed, while his companion waved and yelled. The first man set down his luggage and made a trumpet of his hands. "Hold the boat! We want to get on! Passenger! Passenger!" he brayed.

The little *Caroline* slowed, crept along on the current, her smokestacks giving forth black smoke. The Dill brothers' ferry was on the opposite shore, just arriving with passengers. Abe was busy ferrying the stagecoach across the creek.

"How're we goin' to get out to that there steamboat?" demanded the stouter of the two men, of no one in particular, but Abe was nearest. The stage driver paid his ferry fare and Abe turned to the excited and anguished men.

"We got to get on that boat—we're goin' to New Orleans and we got to get aboard! She's waitin' for us—where's the ferry at, young man? Oh, over there? It'll never get back here in time to set us on that boat. Oh, gosh, she's goin' on without us! What'll we do?"

"I'll carry you out to the boat, sir," spoke up Abe. "I only got me a little skiff, but it'll carry you and your baggage and put you safe aboard. The ferry'll never get back in time. The steamboat's still waiting. Hurry up!"

The men grabbed up their satchels, shoved their beaver hats down securely over their ears and dashed with Abe to the small rowboat. They piled in awkwardly, almost swamping the craft, and Abe rowed out fast, breasting the current, while the steamboat, slowly moving downstream with the current, tried to hold back and wait. Abe was dripping and his hair kept getting in his eyes.

"Can't you hurry?" the stouter man cried nervously. He was holding with both hands to the sides of the boat.

"I'm going as fast as I can. Only I got the current coming at me, and a wind, too. But we'll make it. They're waiting."

They made it. The two men were helped aboard, and one turned with his thanks to the young boatman.

"Here, boy," he cried and threw two heavy silver half-dollars into the bottom of the rowboat, where they chinked together with a most lovely sound of wealth.

Abe waved and shouted his thanks. He carefully gathered up the money and put it into his pocket.

Imagine! Making a whole dollar in a few minutes! A dollar was a lot of money. He'd have had to work almost three days for James Taylor to earn that much, would have labored mighty hard in the bargain. Now, with hardly any effort at all, he was rich. It wasn't just the dollar, but the possibilities of making money which it revealed. If a hard-working man could earn a dollar in less than an hour, just think what he could do, in the right business, if he applied himself and really worked! In a pleasant daze, Abe rowed back to shore and sat dreaming on the seat of the skiff until the Dill brothers rudely jogged him out of his revery.

"Hey, you, Lincoln, we saw you take our passengers!" Lin Dill shouted from the bank above. "You ain't got no license to run a ferry on the Ohio River! We got a mind to lick you here and now, 'cept it wouldn't do no good, with your thick head, and we'd have to do it all over again ever' blame time you decided to go ag'in us and take our fares!"

155

"Let's haul him to court," said Turnbull Dill, grinning evilly down at the alarmed Abe. "Court's in session over to Judge Pate's."

Abe could win a fist fight, the Dills knew; but in a court fight, he might not be so proficient.

"Squire Pate is over in Kentucky, where we live and where we got our ferry license, seein' as how the Ohio belongs to Kentucky, as you'd know if you wasn't such a fool!" growled Lin Dill. "You come along with us, or else we'll send the sheriff with a warrant for your arrest. You comin' peaceable or do we got to call in the law?"

"I'll come peaceable," said Abe morosely, wondering what was going to happen next—and what his paw would say when he heard that his son had been arrested and hauled to court for breaking the law! He wondered, too, if James Taylor would take his job away from him.

It seemed that the ferry would never get across the big bright blue Ohio, which didn't look quite so beautiful this time, and then Abe thought the ferry really had gone mighty fast because they were landing, and Turnbull and Lin Dill were holding on to his arms as if he were trying to run away. He jerked loose, and the two dodged, thinking he was going to hit them. But he just didn't hanker to be led around like a bull with a ring in its nose.

"I don't aim to run away," he said coldly. "You needn't hold on to me like that."

They went to Judge Pate's little, dusty, hot courtroom. The judge was bored. The case was dull. Lucifer Grant was suing Enos Hume for mixing wild-onion seed with the buckwheat he sold him in the spring, and in consequence the buckwheat crop had been ruined, though nobody could prove whether or not the onion seed had been mixed with the buckwheat, as alleged, or if it had been growing in the field all along. As the case ended, the irate Dills marched in with their captive.

"Judge, this here fellow, name of Lincoln, over in Indiana, has done carried folk on the Ohio for pay, and he ain't got no license except on Anderson's Creek over there. He's done taken our fares and passengers and we don't like it!"

"Well, gentlemen," said Judge Pate tiredly, looking kindly at the uneasy tall young fellow and the angry Dills. Judge Pate mopped his neck. His Negro servant brought in a drink of water. A fly buzzed slowly around the judge's perspiring head, and he swatted it away. A thick, dead calm of heat settled over the dusty courtroom.

The Dills shifted on their big feet. Abe Lincoln didn't know what to do with his hands. Then the judge gave him something to do with one of them, at least.

"Gentlemen," said the judge, "do you solemnly swear to tell the truth, the whole truth, and nothing but the truth? Raise your right hands and swear."

"All right, we'll begin with no more formality," said the judge, anxious to be done and get out of the stifling little courtroom. "Young man, tell your part of it."

"Well, sir," began Abe, hunting words and trying to say them right. "I ain't—haven't—been really taking any business from the Dills. I run a ferry for James Taylor on Anderson Creek. I also got me a little skiff I made for myself, and sometimes I take a passenger out to get on a steamboat when it's in the middle of the river and there isn't any way to get out except by my boat. Today I did it again. Only today the Dills took exception to it. Their boat was on the far shore, and the steamboat wouldn't have waited till they got back to set the passengers aboard. So I did it. That's all."

"But, Judge, that's illegal, ain't it?" protested Lin Dill. "He ain't got no license to ferry folk on the Ohio!"

"Is all that he said true?" asked the judge patiently.

"Reckon it is," admitted Lin grudgingly, "but he ain't got no license—"

"I heard you the first time," asserted the judge with dignity. He opened a book which had *Statutes of Kentucky* stamped on the cover and leafed through it until he found what he was looking for.

"Gentlemen," he said, "this young man is not in the wrong. He would have disobeyed the law if he had carried folk from one shore to the other, but he is within his rights when he merely

157

carries a passenger to the middle of the stream, as in the case of a man boarding a steamboat.

"Case dismissed," added the judge. "Charges are two dollars, to be paid by the plaintiffs."

After the angry Dills had paid their fee and departed, Abe stayed on a while and looked with some awe at the law books on the shelves. They were powerful things. They could prove a man guilty or innocent.

All the way back to the river, where the Dills irately made him pay a fare to get to the Indiana side, he thought about what Judge Pitcher had said to him not many days before.

"What on earth do you aim to do with yourself, Abe?" Judge Pitcher had asked in sudden, unexplainable irritation. Abe Lincoln, long legs entwined, his long body slumped on his spine, and intensely silent as he read, was immersed in a heavy book. Abe had looked up at him, puzzled. Then he answered:

"Well, looks to be that I'll turn out about like my paw, with no rightful education and fit only to be a farmer that can't hardly scratch a livin' from the wore-out fields. Or a riverman. I always have hankered to go on the river. I'm strong, and it don't take no great brains to work on a boat, though it likely takes more'n *I* got to pilot a steamboat or be a captain. I would admire to be a steamboat pilot, though, Judge, only I reckon I ain't got no chance."

"Now that's where you're wrong, boy," said the judge warmly, still irritated, though he couldn't have explained why. His fine eyes fired up. "You're so dead wrong, Abe Lincoln, that you're downright pitiful! You may have been born into a family that might expect nothing more of you than that you be a fair-to-middling farmer and a decent, law-abiding man, but you aren't obliged to stop with that. Farmers are all right; we need them. But when a man's got more in his head than what is called for in farming the wilderness and paying his taxes on time, then I say it's a crime if he doesn't use it.

"Here you are, and in spite of the fact that you haven't had more than perhaps a full year in school, you have a brain that takes in everything. You figure out law books that college men have written; you memorize Shakespeare's plays and Henry Clay's and Webster's speeches. You crave learning. That's why you walk sixteen miles to read my books, why you hike yourself over to Boonville and down to Judge Turnham's and round about, goodness knows where, when you smell out the presence of a book or a newspaper. And so, what are you going to do with this education you're giving yourself?"

Abe broke in humbly, confused. "But, Judge, I sure ain't got no—"

The judge in turn impatiently interrupted him. "That's what I mean! Your education's in your head but not on your tongue. Now listen, do you ever hear me saying, 'I ain't got no'?"

Abe shook his head, humbler still.

"I know I can't talk right," he began in discouragement.

"But you can!" the judge had insisted, his eyes alight. "That's why this kind of education you've given yourself is worth so much. You read books written by educated men; they're giving you their learning. Follow what they say, the way they say it. They can teach you, if you'll let them.

"Now, instead of saying, 'I ain't got no,' what should you say?"

"Well, I—ain't—I haven't—I haven't any!" finished Abe in triumph, light dawning in his eager gray eyes. " 'I haven't an education,' I should have said. I'll remember, Judge. And I won't forget this here conversation, ever. I'll watch my language and think before I say a word!" He laughed, and his face glowed with the beautiful inner light which transformed its homeliness into something unforgettable and fine.

"Besides being a riverman," went on the judge, "which you think takes brawn but little brains, what else might you fancy as a life's work?" The judge leaned back in his polished black walnut chair and crossed his broadcloth knees and watched the boy.

"I reckon I'd like to be a lawyer, sir, and maybe get to be a judge like you, or maybe go to the legislature," Abe had ventured slowly, thinking, and finding pleasure in the thinking. This was to his liking, much better than figuring on taking over the farm when Paw got too old, even better, maybe, than going on the river. "But I sure do hanker for the river, too," he had added ruefully, thinking of the allure of the Ohio and the wonders of the steamboats and the mystery of night along the water—and always a new bend beyond and new shores and strange adventures. "I sure would admire to have a trip clear down to New Orleans!"

"Well, why not?" cried the judge. "What you need is to get away, expand your horizons. It all boils down to the same thing. We've got to get you out of the wilderness, and whether you go by stagecoach or by steamboat or on foot, it doesn't much matter. See as much of the world as you can before you settle down to making a living and using the mind God gave you. If you ever find a chance, you take that trip on the river!"

"I might stay on the river!"

"Well, that's for you to decide. And mind, if you do stay on the river, then you've got to work yourself up to a top position there. I won't settle for anything less than that for Abraham Lincoln. Steamboat pilot or captain, no less! Otherwise, you come ashore and learn to speak correctly, study law so you can be a lawyer, and, if I'm not mightily mistaken, fate will take you on from there!"

"Reckon Paw and Dennis'll rag me about my fine talk," said Abe wryly, harking back to the original subject of the conversation, "not to mention Squire Hall and the Grigsbys and some others I could mention. They'll think I'm settin'—setting—myself up mighty grand, talking like a judge."

"Let them," said Judge Pitcher blandly.

"Well, I reckon I'll have to. I can lick the Grigsbys and some others, but I can't lick Paw."

"I know, you're a fighter," the judge had said, just a trifle sadly. "You're the strongest boy in Spencer County, and you don't hesitate to let everyone know it. I've heard of your fights, Abraham Lincoln. Well, you go ahead and fight if you must, but remember that fighting with fists and muscles is fighting with only part of you. You've got to fight with your mind, too, and if your mind can't get the best of you in a fight with your inner self, in fights between you and your conscience, then your muscles aren't much good. Don't you forget it, Abe. If you can't lick yourself, then you're weak, and any man with a stronger mind than yours can finally lick you, too."

Abe had looked startled. The thought had never occurred to him before. The judge had given him almost more than he could digest, but it was good meaty stuff. He had to be able to lick himself before he could think to lick someone else; that was good. And he'd got to get out of the wilderness before he could make something of himself. And he'd got to watch his language—not say "ain't got no," and to put on all the "gs." That was going to be mighty hard, but it was a challenge to try anyway, and if the judge thought he could amount to something that way, he'd surely try.

CHAPTER SEVENTEEN

THE YEAR of Our Lord, 1828: Andrew Jackson pursued his political campaign that would put him in the White House the following year. Over in Europe, Franz Schubert died, and with him perished music unheard. The first locomotive was being perfected that in the following year would travel on rails which would begin to stretch out across America. In England, friction matches had been in use for a year, and no longer would men have to strike a light with flint and steel. Peru was at war with Bolivia and Colombia, and in the Pigeon Creek community, in backwoods Indiana, Sally Lincoln Grigsby, in January of that year, was delivered of a child who died at birth. The next day Sally herself closed her eyes and followed her baby in death.

A grave was hacked in the frozen ground of the Pigeon Baptist Church burying plot, near where an old Indian trail went through. The forest stood close about, grim and bare in the winter cold. The baby was buried with her, in Sally's thin, tired, enfolding arms.

Abe was shocked. He was stunned. He could not believe what had happened. Death was something that came to the old, to the ill, to—to other people. His mother had died, but to his young eyes she had seemed old, and he knew she had been ill. But Sally—Sally was young. She had looked forward with such pleasure to her baby's coming—and then it was all over, as suddenly and finally as if you had put out a candle. The crinkling smile would come no more on her face; the little baby had gone, too, before

162

it had even breathed. Abe attended the burying, and he went about his chores; but he felt as if something inside himself had died with Sally's going. She was that other part of him, that link with the existence in Kentucky, that mutual understanding of life which had lain so closely between them.

He had just begun to climb out of the morass of grief and despair, when his friend, Allen Gentry, up and married Ann Roby, who had never failed to make Abe's heart beat a double-time staccato whenever he saw her. Ann was always kind to Abe. She was sweet; but she always laughed a little at him, too. And when he asked her to walk out with him, she usually, though not always, turned him down. Now she had married Allen Gentry. Well, if little Annie Roby was bound to marry somebody that wasn't Abraham Lincoln, he could think of no one who would be better to her than his friend Allen, a good man and well fixed. Abe knew very well that, even if he himself might like to marry Ann, he was too poor to support a wife—and, besides, his father would never let him do anything so rash.

He was glad, in a way, that it was Allen. If Abe had had to stand by as he did with Sally marrying that Aaron Grigsby, who had killed her; as he had stood by, oozing disapproval, when that no-account kin of his, Squire Hall, had married sweet little Tilda Johnston, and then had had to see Ann Roby wed to some no-good—he'd have done something desperate and rash. But Allen was all right.

When seventeen-year-old Tilda bore her first child, Sarah assisted her daughter, with Elizabeth to stand by, and Mrs. Crawford for moral support. The children were sent over to Grigsbys. Except for Tilda, the whole family was tense, for there was still the sharp, bitter memory of what had happened to Sally and her baby earlier that year, and there was no telling, out here so far from a doctor, what would happen. They were all in a state of nerves, even Tom. But Tilda took it calmly, endured her ordeal without undue commotion, produced a lusty boy, then, tired out, turned over and went to sleep.

Later that day, when the children came home, thirteen-year-old John D., and Elizabeth's four—Johnny, six, Sally, five, Nancy, three, and the baby, Harriet, two—John D. asked what they were going to name the new arrival in the already overcrowded cabin.

"Well," said Matilda from her bed, "I reckon maybe we'll call him John."

"John!" burst out John D. in sudden irritation. "I'd like to know what's so wonderful about namin' all the Hanks and Hall and Johnston boy-babies 'John'! I'm fair sick of it. Used to be when someone yelled, 'John,' I could rightly speak up and ask what was wanted. Now—just look! Abe, I ask you, is it fair or ain't it?"

Abe grinned down tolerantly at the perturbed youth.

"Well, it looks to me like you have a good case there," he agreed. "It is getting a mite crowded with Johns hereabouts. If a body piped up and said, 'Hey, John, you want a hundred dollars?' why, all of you would be right there in front, trampling down the weakest. And if somebody yelled, 'John, you come here this minute and get the lashing you so well deserve,' why none of you would know which was meant, and so nobody would come, and then whoever felt you needed a lashing would get madder and madder and likely lash all four of you! Yes, you've got a good case there!" Abe pulled his lower lip and mimicked Judge Breckenridge over in Boonville, when he was pondering a case.

"Now, let's see, how many Johns do we have, anyway? There's Cousin John Hanks who, thank fortune, has the gumption to live in his own cabin, though close enough to get into the confusion. Then there's you, John D., and Dennis and Elizabeth's John, and now Tilda wants to call her young one John. Yes, it is a mite crowded."

"Well, what can we do about it?" complained John D., luxuriating in his self-pity. "Used to be, I was the only John around, and now there sure ain't nothin' o-riginal about that handle!"

"*Hmmmmm*," said Abe, still as Judge Breckenridge. "Well, why not take another name and so remove some of the strain from the John fraternity?"

164

"What name?" cried John D., startled. " 'Twouldn't be legal to take another one."

"Oh, it wouldn't be permanent, just while you're around so many of the same name. So why not call yourself Jack? That's a nickname for John anyway, and it has a right smart sound to it."

"Jack—Jack Johnston . . . Say, Abe, that sounds right as rain. It's got a dash to it, too, like you say. Gee, I wish Maw'd named me that at the start. Jack Johnston—that's me!" He capered about in glee, upset the water bucket and paused suddenly in dismay to survey the mess.

"All right, you Jack or John or whatever you call yourself," his mother said briskly. "You get on to the business end of the mop and get that water sopped up, and then you tote the bucket down to the spring and bring up more. Fast, now!"

After that, there was no John D. in that household. It was considerably easier, too, in conversation and in giving orders, to have one of the Johns eliminated. Jack Johnston, perhaps in keeping with greater dash as represented in his new name, rapidly was growing up into a youth who was knowing far beyond his years, a blond young fellow who delighted in tormenting animals and who liked nothing better for sport than to smash a terrapin against a tree and watch the miserable creature die by inches. He was a youth who took up with doubtful acquaintances and had a decided knack of getting into trouble.

It was later in the summer that Allen Gentry asked Abe if he would go with him to take a cargo-load of produce down to New Orleans in early winter. They would have to wait until Ann had her baby, due in December, but since the flatboat was not yet built—and it would be Abe's job to build it—the time would go fast.

Abe, thinking of one of his dearest dreams coming true, could hardly wait. The ten dollars a month which Allen promised to pay him for his work as crew meant little; it would go to Tom Lincoln, anyway. But it was the getting away on the river at last, of seeing that part of the world New Orleans represented, which sent Abe about his work in a pleasant daze of anticipation and dreams.

In the fall, Abe lived on Allen's farm and helped build the big flatboat, down by the rocky cliffs of the river shore at Rockport. The leaves fell down in the autumn winds, and the river, which had been low, rose beautifully from rains up in West Virginia. The steamboats, which had been held back by the low water, were going by again. Abe got to know them well, felt a familiar friendliness for them, recognized their distinctive whistles, rejoiced at the rhythmic thudding of steam from the 'scape pipes. He always stopped work to wave at the people on the boiler deck and watch how the buckets of the big wheel dug deep and flashed white water, rolling over and over, upstream or down.

The flatboat was finished and straining at her lines. She was eighty feet long and twenty feet wide, and was completely enclosed, like a mammoth houseboat, with a big hickory sweep on top for steering. There was a sandbox for a fireplace inside, with a chimney, and pallets on the floor for Allen and Abe. The rest of the space was for the cargo.

When cold weather set in, droves of hogs were driven to the field near the flatboat landing and butchered. Then the meat, put down in barrels, salted, was loaded on board the big boat. Corn was brought in barrels, and apples, too, and kegs of cider and vinegar and whiskey. Lard was rendered down and packed away in kegs. There was tobacco and there was even a supply of maple sugar, saved from last winter's crop. It was going to be a large, profitable load, once it was finished and on its way.

Abe fidgeted. He grew more and more restless. It was getting late in the year. It was cold at night. If the river should freeze up hard, as it did when it caught the Boatload of Knowledge up near Pittsburgh, they'd be stuck. But they couldn't go until Ann had her baby, and he thought the baby was all-fired slow in making its appearance!

CHAPTER EIGHTEEN

On the last day of the year 1828, Abraham Lincoln and Allen Gentry found themselves sailing magnificently down the Ohio River, with the river high, the wind brisk and the spirit of adventure sweetly on the air. At last Abe was on the river, going with the water wherever it would take him, down to meet the Mississippi, and the sense of excitement in his breast surely was no less than that in the breasts of all explorers of rivers when first they set out upon the moving waters.

The flatboat moved briskly with the current. It was only going four or five miles an hour, but it seemed to Abe that the shores were passing by extraordinarily fast. From dawn to dark, Allen navigated the heavy craft around the innumerable bends and past the cliffy shores, past the big cave where pirates often lurked to lure unwary boatmen inside; down to the place where the Ohio became the Mississippi. Nights, they tied up to shore.

"It just ain't safe to try to navigate at night," explained Allen. "Too many snags, and no way to know when another boat's goin' to bump into you or you into it, and anyway, now that the steamboats are goin' night and day, it just ain't safe. They never see you till they're on top of you, and then it's too late. Down on the Mississippi we'll tie up with other boats at towns. It's protection against bandits and pirates and such. But we'd get down to New Orleans twice as fast if we could go night and day."

"I'm in no hurry." Abe smiled, taking his turn at the steering oar and loving the strong feel of the hickory sweep under his hands. He was thrilled with the power within himself which was growing with every mile of the Ohio River sliding under him, taking him away from the close, irksome confines of home. It was a lovely life, with nothing much to do but keep the boat where she belonged, eat and sleep and watch the country go by.

Abe had thought the Ohio was big, but the Mississippi—it was tremendous! It was galloping ahead, yellow-brown and full, with black snags riding along like live things—whole trees, sometimes— and other snags and trees lying in the water and sticking into the air enough to be seen before you hit them. Worst of all, though, Allen warned, were the hidden snags. The big river was full of them, anchored in the bottom and sharp as knives to rip the bottom out of a steamboat. They could wreck a flatboat, too, but not so easily, since a flatboat didn't extend into the water so far. You could get hung up on a snag, though, and stay there till doomsday, unless there was a big enough rise in the river to float you off.

Down the Mississippi . . . around its horseshoe bends till you felt you'd meet yourself coming back . . . warm, now, more like spring than winter . . . a couple of days of rain, and then a feeling almost as of blossoms in the air. . . . Plum Point Reach to be gotten through, the worst stretch of snags on the whole Mississippi River . . . Memphis . . . Vicksburg . . . Natchez . . . the bottomland cockleburs full of bright green little paroquets, the gabby-birds, busily eating the seeds and chirruping gaily in the warm sunshine . . . Baton Rouge, the river bigger and deeper than ever under the flatboat.

"They say the river's 200 feet deep here," commented Allen.

A few miles below Baton Rouge, he remarked:

"I want to stop down here at Madame Duchesne's plantation; she's bought stuff off me before. She's a genteel old lady who lives here and runs a whole plantation by herself; got a lot of slaves and knows how to treat them, and they do her work. She most often asks me in to have dinner with her when I come. She's nice that way, nothin' high-toned or proud. She'd as soon ask in a riverman to dinner as invite the president of the United States, I guess. Maybe she gets lonesome way back here; I don't know."

"Well, you aren't a common riverman, Allen," protested Abe. "You're a big landowner. I doubt me she'd invite some of the river trash we've seen on the keelboats, for instance. There's rivermen *and* rivermen. You're different, got some education and all. She could see you're quality, same as her."

"Well, not quite the same." Allen grinned, flattered. "Wait till you see that house of hers—like a palace, I guess, when you think how we live in Indiana. There—that's her place over behind the levee, where you see the big oak trees full of that long gray moss. We'll steer over to her landing and then I'll go ashore and see if she wants some apples or maple sugar or whatever. She most always does."

Abe waited on the boat. The house was stately behind the trees of a long avenue leading up from the waterfront, and there were flowers in bloom—imagine, flowers in January! He wished Sarah Lincoln could see them. She always set such a store by flowers.

When Allen came back he had three Negroes with him. He was grinning broadly. So were his escorts.

"She's home, and she's invited us both to have dinner with her, Abe. What do you think of that? We're sure in luck. Her men'll haul the barrels she wants up to the house. The boat'll be safe here; two of them'll stand guard whilst we're up there. Get your face and hands washed and your hair slicked down as well as you can. Here, let me see if I can get your pants-legs to come down and meet your moccasins. Golly but you're tall! No wonder your maw can't keep up with the way your legs is growin', and no wonder them pants look so high-water."

"Oh, well," sighed Allen, sitting back on his heels, giving up on Abe's pants-legs, "I guess I can't make you over in a minute. Long's you're clean, that's the best we can do."

He polished off his own hands and face in the river, combed his hair, brushed his jacket, and the two, leaving a pair of slaves to look after the boat, walked jauntily up the long avenue of oaks to the beckoning pillars of the white plantation house.

From the moment he padded up the steps in his moccasins and walked across the broad, shady porch of Madame Duchesne's house,

Abraham Lincoln felt as if he were in a dream, in another world. The tall, thin, dignified woman who met them at the door took his hand in her slim, bony one, gave it a firm pressure which belied the delicacy of that hand and looked up at his earnest, embarrassed face.

"I bid you welcome, Mr. Lincoln," she said courteously, as if he was the finest gentleman in the land. "Allen has told me about you, and I am pleased to make you welcome. Come into the library and be comfortable while I tell Delphine our guests have arrived. I have so few guests—I'm flattered to have you here!" Smiling, the tall figure moved out of the room and left Allen and Abe standing awkwardly in the middle of the deep red velvet carpet, which was soft as new grass under their feet. The great windows were draped with more red velvet, with lace hanging over the panes—so much glass, letting in so much light.

Abe thought of the one glass window which Sarah Lincoln had fought to have, but this big house—this palace—was full of them. And the walls: books on shelves that went to the ceiling. Even at Judge Pitcher's, he had never seen so many books. His fingers fairly tingled to reach out and open one, and then he would sit down and read on and on, until he had devoured them all. There was an almost physical ache in his middle, looking at those books and knowing that he should never have the opportunity to read any of their tantalizing pages.

Madame Duchesne was at the door again.

"Will you please come in now—Delphine tells me dinner is served. Here, let Joseph take your hats. How careless of me!" she added, relieving Allen and Abe of their battered headgear, on which they had retained a tight clutch.

The two young men followed her, mute, out to the dining room which lay at the end of the long, carpeted hall. That hall alone, Abe was figuring in his mind, was bigger than his whole house back on Pigeon Creek, and not a speck of bare wood showed. The walls and ceiling were papered with some sort of fine, figured stuff, and soft carpeting covered the floor. The woodwork was even painted. He surreptitiously ran a finger over it. Yes, paint, not whitewash—

whitewash came off on your finger.

They were seated around an oval table on which a wonderful white tablecloth hung clear to the floor. There were big, folded white linen napkins, too. Abe watched what Madame Duchesne did with hers and quickly followed suit, laying his open on his lap and hoping his old boat clothes wouldn't ruin it.

Abraham Lincoln had never eaten such a meal in his life. The Negro girl kept bringing platters of things to him, until he had heaped his plate high—fried chicken and sweet potatoes cooked in some sort of sweet syrup and pink ham slices rimmed with white fat edged with pepper and spice. There was a bowl of collard greens cooked with pork jowl and hot biscuits that were light enough to float off his plate if he let go of them; there was honey to put on them, too, and preserves, and butter that was sweet and fine, laid out in a ruby glass dish and imprinted with the picture of flowers and a butterfly. There was coffee, thick, boiling-hot, black coffee of such strength that Abe batted his eyes and then took another cautious sip, wondering at such a potent brew.

When the two young men had eaten, while Madame Duchesne only picked at her food and kept up a running conversation with both of her guests, the girl took out the plates and then—as if all that wasn't more than plenty—came back with dishes of a kind of pie which Abraham Lincoln had never tasted in his life.

"Ma'am," he asked hesitantly, after his first bite of the dark, sweet, custardy confection with nut-meats in it, "this is the best pie I ever ate—what do you call it? I'd admire to tell my mother about it when I get back!"

"That's pecan pie, Mr. Abe," she said, smiling. "I'll write down the receipt for you, and you can take it to your mother."

Somehow the day was pretty well past and the sun middleways of the afternoon sky before either young man thought of moving on. Abe had contrived to get into the library, and, although he found that a lot of the books were printed in a foreign tongue, he lost himself in one he could read. By the time they managed to break away, it was too late to cast off and start on their journey again. They'd be as safe at Madame Duchesne's plantation landing as anywhere, if not safer, so they resolved to stay where they were.

Their gracious hostess waved good-bye to them from between the white pillars, and they went back to the boat. They thanked the Negroes who had guarded it, and Allen gave them a little money and went aboard. Everything was shipshape and as he and Abe had left it.

When it grew dark, the pair turned in for the night. "It's too warm to sleep down here," said Abe, disliking the idea of going to sleep in close, tight quarters, in company with a lot of barrels of pork, vinegar, whiskey and suchlike for bed companions, when he could have the whole southern sky and the whole river outside. Allen felt the same way, so they took their bedding up on the top of the boat and spread it out.

Abe lay for a long time, it seemed to him, staring straight up into the boundless blackness of the star-sprinkled sky. He felt the urgent breathing of the river under him. He felt one with the sky and the river, as if there were only those two entities left and he between them. Then he fell asleep. Allen had been slumbering long since.

It was Abe who heard the footsteps at the far end of the boat, heard the low tones of men talking. Someone was out there, likely up to no good! If they were Madame Duchesne's slaves, come with a message or something, they'd have hailed the boat, not crept aboard so sneakily and silently. Abe nudged Allen.

"*Shhhhh!*" he whispered, when Allen woke with a muttered exclamation. "There's someone forward on the boat, don't know how many. There's a crab-apple club lying over near you, and I've got me a club, too. Get up easy and come along. If we can surprise 'em before they know we're on to them, we'll have the advantage."

The night was so bright with stars that it made a light of its own, and the river picked up enough starshine to glow a little, too, so that the boat and the trees and the figures of the intruders stood out more blackly than the rest of the darkness. Abe quickly counted—one, two—glory be, there must be at least seven of them, and only two to defend that costly cargo!

He crouched and ran forward lightly, but the men saw him and with a roar they leaped upon him. Allen was right there with him. Abe knocked one assailant down and he rolled into the river; Abe could hear him splashing about and swimming toward shore. Another jumped Abe from behind and was forcing him backward to snap his spine, when he twisted free and got one of his Indiana wrestling holds and flung the man after his companion. Abe and Allen had discovered by this time that the marauders were Negroes, big, silent, gorilla-like fellows, who made guttural, animal-like noises as they fought.

Allen was having his own troubles, but seemed to be coming out all right with the crab-apple club. Abe found his where it had fallen from his hand, and he laid about him with it. Then suddenly he was knocked down with a violent blow above his eye which blacked him out momentarily. He came to quickly, fighting to keep from going under again with the pain and the concussion of the blow.

Suddenly there was a racket up on the avenue, echoing down from the plantation house. Madame Duchesne's slaves, armed with torches and clubs, were coming on the run down the oak alley, but when they arrived the intruders had vanished. One of Madame's Negroes, coming home late, had passed along the levee above the flatboat and had heard the muted violence of the attack. Knowing he could do little to help alone, he had raced for assistance. But it was all over. Allen was without cuts or too painful bruises, but Abe's head ached as if he had been hit with a maul, and blood was streaming down his face. He felt gingerly of his eye, hoping he still had it. There was so much blood, he couldn't be sure.

In the light of the torches held by the anxious slaves, he got the blood washed off enough to be sure that he really did have both eyes and could see out of them. The cut kept on bleeding profusely, however, until he plastered some salt on it, and then, with a rousing degree of sting, it finally quit. The cut eventually healed, but Abraham Lincoln was to have the scar of it all his life.

"Thanks for coming to the rescue," said Allen to the Duchesne slaves, who ducked their heads, grinning. "I don't think we'll be bothered again, whoever they were. But just to make sure, I reckon we'll cast off right now and be on our way. I'd admire if you'd tell

Madame Duchesne we sure appreciated her hospitality, but we'd better get goin'."

Abe, his head still aching like fury, pulled the heavy lines loose from their moorings, dragged them aboard and coiled them. The flatboat moved silently away into the night. Abe, looking back, saw the slaves and their torches standing on the levee, a vivid group of black figures against a black night, picked out in flame.

The dark river seemed as wide as the world and merged with the sky, with only a thin rim of trees marking the shore. Stars were mirrored in the ebony water that sped along with a sibilance that was different from its daytime talk. The water curved silkenly away from the bow, and only the squeak of the steering oar made a sharp voice in the night.

Abe Lincoln and Allen Gentry, steering the heavy flatboat around the curving waterfront of New Orleans to the landing designated for flatboats, nosed into a berth, paid their wharfage fee and stepped eagerly ashore. The waterfront was a forest of masts and steamboat smokestacks, big boats and small lined up for miles along the *batture*, forming a necklace around the throat of the Queen City of the Mississippi, the City of Sin, New Orleans, in the winter of 1829.

There was so much to look at, so much to do, there were so many ways to turn, that young Abe Lincoln felt confused and a trifle dizzy. He tagged after Allen Gentry, almost afraid to be left alone in the mingling throng of often wild-looking, vari-colored people. Allen, however, proceeded in a business-like manner to sell the rest of his produce and then sold the flatboat itself, which would be taken apart for lumber.

With a good supply of silver dollars heavy in his pockets, Allen Gentry had accomplished the purpose of his trip to New Orleans.

It was customary for flatboatmen to spend a period of time in the city before starting back north to their homes, and this rip-roaring holiday in the tough, relentless, ruthless old river city often was their ruination. Frequently a man who had safely brought his year's produce to New Orleans for more than a thousand miles downstream and in satisfaction had pocketed his money, finally left town

—if he left it alive—with nothing remaining. New Orleans was out to take the riverman's money away from him, and it seemed that, in all conscience, he was willing and ready to part with it in the many and diverse ways in which a river city contrives to separate a man from his wealth.

Allen Gentry, however, was different from most. He was no hired hand whose responsibility ended with the disposal of the cargo at New Orleans. Allen was the owner of the cargo, he and his father, and it was Allen's responsibility and desire to get home as quickly as possible with the full amount of money from the sale of the cargo-load, less the amount it might take to get him there via the next steamboat heading north up to the Ohio.

Although Abe Lincoln might have wished to linger for weeks in the fascinating old city, Allen was in a hurry to get home. There was not only the money to be carried there safely over half a continent of space in which there were more than enough bandits waiting to take it away from him, but he had Ann, his wife, waiting for him, and the new baby, his first son, waiting too. Allen was eager to get back.

"I'd sure hate for the baby not to know his own daddy," he said apologetically.

The steamboat *George Washington* was due to start north the very next day. Allen immediately signed on as passenger. Abe, mentally counting over the amount of money he'd have coming to him when he got off at Rockport, didn't see how he'd have much left to hand over to his father, if he paid steamboat fare out of it. He talked to the captain of the *George Washington*.

"Certainly, young man, we always need help aboard," said the captain. "You help stoke the boilers and go ashore at wooding stops and tote cord wood and you can earn your passage clear. Maybe, if you look sharp, you might even earn a few dollars extra when we load or unload."

Abe grinned, delighted. Riding a steamboat had been his dearest wish ever since he first saw one on the Ohio River, a wish which had expanded like a bubble inside him while he worked on the ferry. Now, incredibly and unbelievably, he, Abraham Lincoln of the

Indiana wilderness, a nobody and a nothing, actually was down in New Orleans and was about to take a thousand-mile trip on a steamboat, just to get back home! In spite of the lure of the city lying back of the river, he would have been more than willing to go aboard at once and get started on the voyage up the Mississippi.

CHAPTER NINETEEN

After what he had seen and done, home looked dull and cramped and incredibly small to Abe. He felt so different himself after his experiences, he almost expected everyone and everything also to be changed.

But changes, like yeast, were nevertheless subtly at work. He found that Cousin John Hanks, who never did anything rashly or hurriedly, had decided to move to Illinois. John was sick of trying to farm in Indiana, of working himself half to death on poor land and reaping only miserable crops. Now Illinois, he said, hadn't such heavy forest growth and was more level, everyone told him, and the earth was black and deep. He was going to take his family and go, in a month. If it was all he thought it would be, he'd send word to Thomas Lincoln, and Tom could come out later on and take up land near by.

For Tom Lincoln was worried. Not only were his fields not as productive as he would wish, but the spring was going dry every year or so. There had been, besides, a flare-up of milk sickness in the summer of 1828 which had scared Tom Lincoln more deeply than he would have admitted. He'd had enough of milk sickness, and the autumn of 1828 had had more of it round about than there had been ten years before when he'd lost Nancy. He'd heard news from up on White River, how the promising town of Hindostan, near the falls of the White River, had been all but wiped out with the sickness, and the survivors had been so alarmed that the county seat had been moved away, and the town was accursed, doomed to nothing. Folk were dying in other places; communities were perishing.

It was terrible, living in a land like this where disease struck and no one knew what to do about it, but just let folk lie there and die. Tom was ready to get out, to go some place where it was safer—the land healthier, the life easier.

"You go see how it is in Illinois," he told John Hanks, "and let me know soon as you're sure. Wait till fall and see if there's aught of milksick, and then you let me know."

When word came back, via a traveler bound for Cincinnati and passing through Spencer County, that John Hanks said the land in Illinois was good and unbelievably rich, and there was no milksick, and that he had taken an option on some land which Tom Lincoln might like, Tom made up his mind as to what he was going to do.

He was getting old to be moving again, but what was a man to do when the land he bought didn't work out right, or else he lost it? He hadn't lost the Indiana farm, it was true, but neither was it all paid for, and the crops were never very good on it. The uneven ground was hard to farm. Sometimes Tom wondered what he had seen in it in the first place, but that was fourteen years ago, and he'd forgotten. He had simply held to his motto—"When you make a bad bargain, just hug it the tighter."

John Hanks had said, "Come," and Tom Lincoln made ready to go. He set Abe to cutting wood to build three wagons. Abe cut down a big oak and whipsawed great disks from its massive trunk to make wheels. He had them shod with iron bands, and fastened them to the axles. Abe and Dennis cleated planks together to build wagons which would hold the women and children and household goods, for when a Lincoln moved, the whole family moved, too. Tom would not hear of it when Dennis figured maybe he'd stay in Indiana, though for a while Dennis had been eager enough to get away when he saw himself losing most of his cows and calves in last summer's epidemic. But Dennis cannily figured that he and Elizabeth and their four children might just take over Tom's land and finish payments on it eventually. Tom, however, had already arranged to sell the place to Charles Grigsby, and he wasn't going to hand it over to Dennis Hanks at a loss. Dennis had sponged off him for a good many years, he and his tribe, without contributing a great deal either in labor or in cash.

The winter of 1829 went by, a bitterly cold and uncomfortable winter, in which the children were eternally sick with colds or the bold-hives, or something. Abe was getting impatient. The cabin was more cramped than he could ever remember. He was thankful that he had learned to read in a blab-school, because if anyone could read and concentrate in a din like that, then he could do it easily in the Lincoln household of thirteen people who were forever jawing and yammering at each other, with the children quarreling or crying or coughing. There was enough space for all of them to sleep, with the trundle beds shoved under the big beds in daytime, and room in the loft—space to cook and eat and gather around the fire also. What more did a body want, Tom demanded.

Abraham could think of a number of things, remembering Madame Duchesne's gracious home and Judge Pitcher's house, and some others he'd seen, but you couldn't tell Tom Lincoln that. He'd only blow up in a fury and shout that Abe had ideas too big for his breeches. So Abe worked on the wagons, asking advice of Josiah Crawford, who was an expert wagoner by trade, and Tom and Sarah took a quick trip back to Elizabethtown, to sell some land which Sarah still owned. With the money, they bought a yoke of oxen to haul the wagons. Judge Turnham would buy the hogs and most of the stock, and part of the pay would be another yoke of oxen.

Meanwhile, Abe had been clerking over at the Jones-Gentry store ever since the last spring's plowing. But he was anxious to get started on the trip to Illinois.

"If we went now," he suggested on February twelfth to his father, who was sitting silently, spitting now and again into the fire, "we could go on frozen ground and wouldn't get mired down in the mud when it thaws. The bottoms across the Wabash are going to be a mess, come the breakup."

"You mind your own business, Abe Lincoln," growled Tom. "I'm makin' the decisions in this family, and I say we'll go on the first day of March, and no sooner."

"All right, Paw," said Abe tightly, turning on his heel. He went out into the brisk winter air and walked and walked, passing his mother's grave, up on the hill near the deer trail. He paused there a bit, reflectively, not sadly, because he didn't remember her very well, except with an introspective remembering, a timeless vision of having and losing, of living and dying, which the sunken grave on the hilltop represented to him. His mind was filled with the splendid achievements which he had absorbed from books he had read and the talks he'd had with men like John Pitcher and Josiah Crawford and Colonel Jones and James Gentry and Judge Graham, who believed in him and told him he could go ahead and become a big man if he stuck to it. But all this seemed to fall away and leave nothing but the shell of discouragement when he came into the presence of his father.

Today was Abraham Lincoln's birthday, his twenty-first birthday, unnoted in the family except by Sarah, who had kissed him lovingly and told him how proud she was of him. But in Abe it meant a turning point, a point he had been waiting for and working for as long as he could remember. All those books he'd drunk up as if they were wine, intoxicating him with their splendor and the worlds they opened out to him had been leading up to this day, for when he attained his majority, when he became twenty-one at last, he could vote. He was his own master, and he was no longer his father's bound boy, held by the chains of duty to work for Tom Lincoln, obey his father, give all his money to him, follow him, emulate him—but no, they couldn't make him be like his father, worthy though he was. He didn't have to be like his father; he was himself, and now that he was of age, he could express that self.

"But I don't know what I want, really," he mused aloud to the silent winter trees and the sunken grave, to the crows flying over in the winter sunshine. "Now that I'm old enough to do what I want—what *do* I want, anyway?"

He paced. He tramped. He scuffed through the dead pea vines, matted down and softened from having been under snow which had gone off a week ago. He walked, thinking, resenting, hating, feeling unutterably mournful, talking to the redbirds and regretting the kind of fate that put him in the wilderness, with no chance to make something of himself. He had to admit that he had a love for the wilderness—an affection for the birds and animals he had come to know during his days of work in the woods, a love for the trees and most especially for his favorite, the sugar maple; a delight in the vastness of sky and the permanence of earth—but it was not enough. Something beyond the wilderness was forever calling.

Well! He stopped among the pea vines, a sudden thought hitting him. Here he was railing against life, when it was really up to him. If there was anything worth while in him, then he might as well accept the fact that it was for him to use. Other men and women had been kind and had helped him along with books and encouragement and good talk and work, but it was up to him, really, from now on. Maybe it was like Judge Pitcher said—he had to get out of the wilderness. Maybe going to Illinois would do it. At least, now he was twenty-one, a man at last, beholden to no other.

In pride and power, he went with purposeful strides back down the trail to the overfull cabin. Tom Lincoln, bent over with a crick in his back which had been paining him for days, opened the door and shouted at him:

"You, Abe! Where you been? Git back to work on that there wagon! Think you got forever? Git busy before I come out and thrash you!" The latter was just talk, Abe knew, but it was embarrassing for a grown man to hear it from his own father.

"All right, Paw," he said obediently. Time enough for independence. It would take a while for Tom Lincoln to realize that his son couldn't be ordered around any more. But Abe would follow along gracefully until the time came and he could break away.

"And when I break away," he vowed grimly, swinging the maul to split a log into rough planks, "I'll break away for good and all!"

The day before the departure, when Abe went for the last time over to Gentry's store to say good-bye, he laid in a supply of needles, pins, cheap knives, pearl buttons, thread, ribbons, and some rock candy and horehound drops.

"We're going through a lot of settlements," he told Colonel Jones and James Gentry, "and maybe I can turn a penny by selling things the womenfolk'll need. As long as we'll look like a peddler's train, we might as well have something to sell so the folk won't be disappointed!"

It was frosty and cold when the caravan set out. Sarah was the last to leave the house. She had gone back inside for one final look around, to see if anything had been missed. She paused for a moment, then stepped over the worn threshold, closed the big door softly behind her and slipped the latchstring out. The house was suddenly lonely and dead, empty and deserted of life.

The ironbound wheels of the three heavily loaded wagons groaned and screamed as, greaseless, they turned with the great hickory axles. The oxgoads snapped like pistol-shots in the early morning chill.

The oxen strained at their yokes going up hills and held back properly on the downgrade. The children screamed and waved to the Crawfords and the Turnhams. Mrs. Turnham came out with a parcel of fresh maple sugar for the children to eat, for the sap had been running two weeks before, and the sugar trees of Spencer County had given up their supply of sweets. Abe waved a long arm to everyone he saw. The oxen which had belonged to Judge Turnham whuffed and rolled their eyes when they went past the old familiar barn. The screeching of the wheels could be heard almost a mile away.

It was when they turned into a well-worn, level road leading toward Polk Patch that something vaguely familiar stirred in Abraham Lincoln's mind. They were on the old Buffalo Trace. He'd seen parts of it on his travels around southern Indiana, knew that it crossed at New Albany and was connected with the old Wilderness Road down in Kentucky. He had heard his father tell of how he and his father and the family had followed the Buffalo Trace and the Wilderness Road up from Virginia into Kentucky, long ago.

The same thing must have come into Tom's mind, too, for he looked over at his tall son, who looked back at him, and there was a sudden, brief bond of kinship.

ANOTHER JUMPED ABE FROM BEHIND AND WAS FORCING . . . HIM BACKWARD . . .
WHEN HE GOT ONE OF HIS INDIANA WRESTLING HOLDS. . . .

HE PAUSED AND LET THE CROWD **ROAR. HE STOOD** THERE ON THE STUMP . . . AND GRINNED AND **THEN BOWED** IN COURTLY FASHION.

"You know, boy, we're on that old Buffalo Trace again. Funny thing, ain't it, how it's had a part in this here family? We all come up into Kentucky on parts of the Trace, and now here we go again, still travelin' after the buffalo, headin' toward Illinois this time. I hear tell the Trace Road goes all the way to the Mississippi River, but we won't follow it that far—not this time, anyway!" Tom laughed.

Before the end of the first day, Abe could see that one of the oxen which Thomas Lincoln had taken in trade from Judge Turnham was getting homesick. Abe knew the signs . . . the farther away from home the ox was getting, the more often it rolled its eyes back in that direction.

Next morning, when Abe untied the Turnham ox to get it yoked, the critter turned tail suddenly, muttered in its throat, rolled its eyes, and started off in a steady, rocking gait in the general direction of Pigeon Creek. Abe took off after it.

"I won't be long!" he yelled back over his shoulder. Thomas, Squire, Dennis, and Jack just stood there, petrified in their own jobs of getting ready for the morning's departure, their mouths open.

"That blamed ox!" muttered Tom. "Hope Abe catches it!'"

"I'd bet on the ox." Squire Hall grinned. "Got a head start all right."

"Yeah, but look at the way Abe's shortenin' the distance," contradicted Dennis, squinting into the morning sunshine until he could no longer see his long-legged kinsman racing over the hilly Buffalo Road after the delinquent ox.

"Quit your jawin' and git busy," growled Tom. "Abe'll be back afore you're ready, rate you set around chewin' the fat over nothin'.'"

Abe was downright angry and considerably out of breath when he finally got to Judge Turnham's place again. The runaway ox, which hadn't exerted itself unduly, having had a good start—and more wind than Abe—was placidly champing hay in the barnyard. Judge Turnham, just getting up, hastily threw on his pants and came out to see what was wrong. Abe was trying to corner the ox, who neatly sidestepped him every time.

"You'll never catch him that-a-way," contended Judge Turnham, who had been joined by David and the rest of the family, grinning delightedly to see what Abe would do—Abe always knew what to do. He was good with animals, but this ox wasn't interested in being treated well. It simply wanted to stay where it was.

Abe got behind the ox and slapped its rump, and the animal whoofed and thundered into the barn. Then Abe closed the barn door and scrambled up on the broad ledge just above it.

"Now you open the door," he said to David. "And then you get behind that ox and scare him so he'll run outside again."

"What you aimin' to do up there, Abe?" piped up little Martha Turnham.

"You get out of the way, Martha, honey, so you don't get trampled! Hurry now! That's right, get out of the way, because that pesky ox is going to come out running. All right, Dave, turn him loose!"

David roared at the harried ox, who lumbered wildly out of the door. Just as he passed under the ledge, Abe dropped down astride him.

"*Yee-aye-eee! Ya-hooo!*" Abe yelled, gripping the ox with his long, bony legs, crouching, holding the bridle with one hand and slapping the ox's rump with his hat. He lay low, yelling like a Choctaw on the warpath, and the ox, with wild eyes, thudded out of the barnyard and onto the road, back up the trail along which it had pulled the wagon the day before.

The Turnhams stood in the barnyard laughing uproariously at the sight of the lanky young man riding the ox and at the same time skillfully steering the animal in the general direction of the wagon train.

By the time he and the wild-eyed, lathered ox pounded up to the waiting family, Abe was laughing so hard he almost fell off his mount. The ox came to a halt, puffing and blowing and rolling its eyes at its rider. Abe patted the animal on the nose and led it over to drink and eat before being yoked with its companion.

"Well, never in my life did I ever see anything like that!" exclaimed Sarah, hands on hips. "Riding an ox! Land of mercy! What will you think of to do next, Abe Lincoln?"

"Well, Maw, there wasn't any other way to get the critter back. It'll be so glad to be shut of my knees in its ribs, it ought to be right good and tractable from now on. As for me, I doubt if I can sit down comfortable for a couple of days! That ox sure isn't very well padded!"

With the oxen pulling steadily and the horses heaving into the traces up the forested hills, the caravan went on.

"I'm going up here and try my luck at this house," said Abe as they approached Petersburg. "These folk are far enough from town to have need of notions, maybe."

It was time to let the animals rest before tackling the next hill, so the caravan waited while Abe footed it up a hill overgrown with last year's jimson weeds. He was greeted by a barking dog and a din from inside the rickety little old cabin. The door flew open and a small, red-haired, scarlet-faced woman, her eyes snapping blue fire and a whip in her hand, poised on the threshold as a meek-faced, rabbity looking, towheaded man, fully a foot taller than his wife, backed out and down to the ground. He was holding up his hands as if to ward off a blow of the whip. From the interior came loud howls of crying children who, still bawling, followed their mother to the door to see what she was going to do next. The thirteen children, who somehow were crammed inside the little one-room cabin, apparently ranged in age, Abe figured swiftly, from a seventeen-year old, lanky, pimply-faced youth to a dirty baby of about a year and a half. The latter was crawling about on the littered floor and, alone of the brood, was not yelling. He sat up, with a faraway look, and with grimy hands shoved a piece of dirty bacon-rind into his mouth.

The snarly-haired woman saw Abe, and everything stopped. The whip was in mid-air, the arm raised. The children paused in their howls, their mouths open as if the howls had frozen there. The man, standing with his back to Abe, who likewise was frozen in his tracks, didn't know what was causing the cessation in the disturbance.

"Now, now, Agnes," he begged. "Ca'm down, woman. I ain't done no harm . . ."

"Shut up, you Amaziah," she ordered. "What do you want?" she

185

roughly demanded of Abe, who wished he could escape with his little supply of ribbons and needles and horehound drops, or become invisible before she lit into him.

"Nothing, nothing, ma'am," he hastened to say, beginning to retreat down the hill. "I merely dropped in to see how things were going with all of you. I trust you all are well?" He removed his cap and bowed.

"Well, you needn't wait," the woman snapped suspiciously. "There's trouble enough here, lots of it, with these here brats actin' like all possessed, and my man as bad as any. But I kin manage, I tell you that! I kin take care of my own affairs without no help from no nosy outsider. And I don't want nobody sneakin' around and tryin' to find out what they kin, neither! Now git!"

"Now, Agnes," murmured the towheaded man, looking sympathetically and apologetically at Abe.

"You shut up!" flared the woman.

The children thereupon resumed their howling, and the oldest boy kicked the dog, who ran yelping under the woman's skirts and upset her neatly. She went down with a thud and a shrill scream. Abe paused for a moment, then ran to help her up, but she was in no mood for help. Giving him a cut of the whip, to which she still held, a cut which glanced off his jacket without doing much more than sting his shoulders, she screeched:

"Let me alone, you sneaky critter, you! Git off my property afore I set the dogs on you! Git, I said!"

"Yes, ma'am," said Abe hastily, and set off in a hurry down the hill, the children's concerted howling growing fainter as he put distance between him and the terrible woman.

"Well, did you sell anything?" asked Tilda, noting his flushed cheeks and the unusual speed with which he came down the weedy hill. "What's your hurry, Abe? They run you off?"

"Law, what a woman!" he exclaimed, wiping his forehead. "I tell you, a few like that and the world would belong to the women! Why, she had thirteen young ones up there and a meek, milk-and-water man, and they were everyone of them scared to death of her. Little and redheaded and a temper to match, and a rawhide whip that she'd likely laid across the seats of every one of the young ones, and was threatening her husband, who's a head taller than she is, if he's an inch! Land! I was glad to get away from there with a whole skin!"

"Didn't she buy nothin'?" asked Jack.

"I didn't stop to ask! When a female's got fire in her eye and a whip in her hand, and is on the warpath like a fighting Comanche, I don't aim to ask her if she'd fancy a pretty ribbon or a paper of needles or whatever! Come on, Paw, let's get on our way. Maybe next place we stop I'll have better luck. If I don't dispose of my stock, Maw'll have enough needles and pins to last her the rest of her life!"

Late in the afternoon, when the bells of the French church sounded pleasantly across the forests south of Vincennes, and their tones came gently to the ears of the people in the Lincoln caravan, Abraham had one of his ideas.

"Since it's getting on near night and we have to stop soon anyway," he suggested, "why not go up to the town and camp close by? I haven't ever been to Vincennes and may never get back, once we cross into Illinois. Anyway, there's a printing press in Vincennes that I would sure admire to see. It'd be something to buy a newspaper right where it was printed, wouldn't it?" he said cannily, and his father flickered a grin back at him. If there was anything Tom relished especially, it was hearing Abe read the newspaper out loud so he could listen to all the things that had been happening, straight out of the print. In that way, the news wouldn't get distorted through half a dozen tellings.

"Sure, Son. Vincennes ain't more than half a mile and we kin get there pretty quick. You go hunt up that printin' press and be sure you bring back a newspaper. That'd be somethin', to get a paper the day it was printed!"

The family camped just at the edge of Vincennes, within sight of the Wabash River, flowing between forested banks. It was chill and damp in the late afternoon and the fires felt good. Abe hurriedly cleaned himself up and walked into town. He asked the first person he met where the printing office was located and hurried to find it before it closed.

In the office of the *Western Sun and General Advertiser*, Abe found the owner, Elihu Stout, running off some handbills. There were stacks of fresh copies of the newspaper near by and the air was permeated with one of the most delicious smells Abe had ever savored, printer's ink. It was an aroma to taste on the tongue and breathe deeply into the lungs.

He stood there awkwardly for a long time while Mr. Stout and his skinny little helper were finishing their job. Wiping his hands, Elihu Stout finally looked up.

"Well, sir?" he asked politely, but somewhat impatiently, putting on his coat. It was supper time and he had worked late to get out the handbills wanted for tomorrow. "What can I do for you?"

"Well, uh," began Abe, embarrassed. "I'm Abraham Lincoln from over near Rockport, and, well, I've been reading your paper for years and thought that since, well, we were in the neighborhood, so to speak, I'd come and see where the paper was printed. I've always wanted a look at a printing press, sir," he said, warming to the subject as his enthusiasm grew and his shyness subsided at the sight of Elihu Stout's kindly face. "And if you don't mind, can I see what type looks like set for printing, and what do you do to make a paper come out like it does?"

Mr. Stout relaxed. He smiled at the tremendously tall young man and his earnestness.

"Here, Willy," he said to his ink-smeared helper. "Show Mr. Lincoln how we ran off those handbills. Show him the types we use for the paper. Won't take long. It's a small press, I'm sorry to say. Some day we'll get a bigger and better one, but till then I guess the *Western Sun* has got to be printed up on this little rattletrap press. It's nigh closing time," he added, as his visitor raptly stared at the blackened rows of type locked in place for the handbill job.

"Yes, sir," said Abe absently, staring. He touched a letter and it came off black on his finger, and that delighted him—to have gotten fresh printer's ink on him right away.

"You got a job open here, sir?" he asked, eyes shining, turning to where Mr. Stout was preparing to go home to supper.

"You want a job?" countered Mr. Stout, looking him over.

"Yes, sir."

"Well, I haven't got one right now, but Willy here vows he won't have any part of the printing game. He's going to St. Louis to get into the fur business, he *says*," Mr. Stout glowered at the inky Willy, who flickered a sheepish grin back at him and wiped his nose with a blackened forefinger, which left a grimy mustache mark across his already dirty face.

"Says there's more money in it," went on Mr. Stout, "as no doubt there is, because being a printer's devil isn't exactly a lucrative job, as you might say.

"Stop in, in a few weeks, Mr., uh, Lincoln," he concluded, turning determinedly toward the door and standing aside while Abe finally took the hint and walked out, his head meanwhile almost scraping the door top. "Maybe there'll be a job open. Good night, sir! Close up shop, Willy, and don't forget to lock the door."

"Yes, sir, thank you," said Abe mournfully, his hopes down in his boots. There was little chance of his being around Vincennes in a couple of weeks.

Mr. Stout was walking away when Abe suddenly remembered his newspaper. If he went back without one to Thomas Lincoln . . .

"Wait, Mr. Stout—I need to buy me a paper! Hey, Willy, don't lock up yet!" he cried.

Impatiently and with resignation, Elihu Stout went back into the little office and picked up a copy of the *Western Sun* from the stack on the counter.

"Here, Mr. Lincoln, take it, with my compliments!" he said. "No, don't pay me," he added, waving off Abe's proffered coins. "Take it and let me get home to my supper, or Mrs. Stout will think I've fallen into the river. And come back later if you really want to learn the printing trade."

The Lincolns crossed the Wabash River at the old, old crossing where the buffalo had been going over for thousands of years, and where Indians had crossed, and where George Rogers Clark and his soaked, half-frozen men had come to take Vincennes by surprise. It was the place where wagons from the East, day after day, were crossing to the West. There was a ferry now, and the Lincoln wagons, one by one, were taken over. Then they struggled up the bank on the Illinois side.

Tom Lincoln was amazed at the level lands which stretched before him. They were only the broad Wabash River bottoms, rimmed with hills, but there was a degree of levelness which he could not remember having seen before, and the mud of the bottoms was black as pitch, almost, where it clogged the ironbound wheels. Across the morass of Purgatory Bottom, a corduroy road had been laid so that wagons would not sink. The logs of the corduroy, however, were flooded, and the water had frozen. Poles stuck in the mud marked the way through what appeared to be a half-frozen, shallow lake. The wagons broke a way through the ice, but the splinters hurt the animals' hocks. The dogs—Tom's hound and Abe's little Ginger —rode in the wagons.

Once they reached higher ground, the going was easier, though the trail was rutted and hard to pull through in the warmer part of the day, when the ground thawed. The caravan turned toward Palestine, and by March eighth they were going north on an old Indian trail to Hutsonville, and then to the village of Paradise.

"When we get to Hutsonville," said Sarah Lincoln wearily from where she sat in one of the wagons, soothing the Hall baby, who had a cold and had been coughing, "we can stay with kinfolk of mine. Aunt Benjamin Sawyer lives there, and I reckon Cousin Phoebe and Cousin Adeline still do. They'd have room to put us up for the night, and I'd relish a chance to sleep on a real bed again. Camping out at this time of year isn't any picnic, Tom Lincoln!"

"You're gettin' soft, Sarah," Tom said loftily. "Now, I mind the time we all come up the Wilderness Road, and my maw, she slept out on the ground every night for a month, and I never heard her complain. She run the risk of an Indian takin' her hair before daylight, too, every night she went to sleep. This generation don't know what hardship is!"

"That's all very well, Tom Lincoln," said Sarah acidly, gently patting John Hall through another coughing spell. "But I feel soft enough to relish a little comfort now and then, and I reckon you do, too, if you weren't so bullheaded in flattering yourself you relish roughing it!'"

After an overnight stop with the kinfolk in Hutsonville, the caravan crossed, painfully and with difficulty, the flooding Kaskaskia River at Willow Ford. Here an erring wheel finally chose to come off. The wagon sagged into the mud and water. Abe, shucking his boots, waded in and personally substituted for the wheel until the oxen dragged the wagon to shore. Then, the damage repaired somehow, the party struggled on, northwest to the village of Decatur, which only a week before had had its post office approved and postal service put into effect.

In the village square, around which were built a dozen log houses and Renshaw's Store, Thomas Lincoln and his family camped like gipsies for the night. The next day they went wearily on, westward, to try to locate John Hanks.

John heard them coming. The greaseless wheels screamed like souls in agony, and John came out to the road to show the travelers where to turn in to his farm.

The following morning, after one of Madeline Hanks's good breakfasts, and with newly arrived meadow larks whistling from the muddy prairie, Tom and Abe and John Hanks went over to look at the land on which John had taken an option for Tom Lincoln.

And Thomas Lincoln stood there on the gently swelling bosom of the Illinois prairie, where the green grasses were just beginning to sprout and the meadow larks were caroling, and he let his hands drop limply to his sides. A fine light came into his broad face which had known so many disappointments.

"Glory be!" he cried, the light glowing as it had not done since he had come long ago to the Knob Creek land and had found it good. "Glory be! This is it! This is the Promised Land! Look at those level fields and the richness in the dirt. Look!" He stooped and gathered up some of the dark earth in his square-tipped fingers, sniffed it and then let it drop slowly to the ground again, grain by grain. "This is what I been lookin' for all my life! There's a river down below the bluff, so's it won't flood the land, and yet there ain't no hills, and all that pretty open country, and plenty timber along the river. John, you were sure enough right. There ain't nothin' like Illinois! And here we stay. I ain't never goin' to move again! Not till they bury me in this here Illinois sod!"

John Hanks had cut cabin logs during the winter. Now they were ready to put up into a house. While the women and children stayed at the Hanks cabin, along with John's wife and young ones, the men worked harder than they had ever worked in Indiana or Kentucky. Squire Hall had been the laziest man in Spencer County, Tom Lincoln used to say with scorn, but even Squire was working at squaring off the logs. Abe toiled from sunup until dark. Dennis worked. So did Tom. Even Jack labored, though it was hard to keep him at it long enough to count. The hound-dog spent his days hunting out the secrets of the Sangamon River woods, with the little dog, Ginger, at his heels.

The cabin was up, was finished. High on the riverbank, with a fine view downstream, it had a good floor, as Sarah's standards demanded, and a good door and an ample loft. The cabin was 18 x 20 feet, a standard size for most pioneer cabins. Sarah had wished that they might build at least a two-room house with a dogtrot between, since so many members of the family were going to be living together again, but Tom made the house just about as he had made the ones in Indiana and Kentucky. He promised to build on a second room next year.

Sarah sighed, her hopes dashed. She knew that if Tom didn't build that extra room now, he never would.

"Dennis says he's goin' to build a place for himself soon," Tom told her. "And so's Squire, when he gets around to it. Then we'll have room and to spare, and I reckon you'll be complainin' that you ain't got no company and are lonesome-like without the young folk around. Never kin suit a woman."

"Squire and Dennis have been talking about building their own houses ever since they married my daughters and moved in with us," commented Sarah. "They've had plenty of chance. If they do it now, I'll likely fall dead with surprise."

The house built, the men lit into the woods and felled and cleared and got ten acres of corn planted before the hot weather came on. Life, for a little while, looked very good.

CHAPTER TWENTY

THAT SUMMER was blisteringly hot, swelteringly humid. Work lagged. The Lincolns sat around in the shade, or sometimes rode into the near-by town of Decatur, where they sat in the shade at Cousin William Hanks's house.

On Independence Day, the whole family, with ample lunch, went to town for the speeches and celebration. In a community of few excitements, Independence Day offered something different, at least—and it was a way in which to forget the heat.

Young America was already fifty-four years old, two years older than Tom Lincoln, and with her increasing years and dignity, it was altogether fitting and proper that the day of her birth should be celebrated.

Dennis Hanks got hold of some gunpowder and set off a charge which shook Decatur. Jack Johnston and some of his new-found cronies made some firecrackers and spit-devils, and set them off among the people who had assembled for the speeches, concentrated in front of James Renshaw's store. The resultant din and cloud of dust, accented by the shrieks of the women and little girls, only added to the day's excitement. Horses tied to the hitching rail snorted and reared to the extent of their tethers, then settled down to switching endlessly at the flies which swarmed everywhere. The oak leaves looked dusty and the grass was turning brown for lack of rain.

"That grass is so dry," Abe remarked, "that I reckon you'd have to lather it up good before you could mow it!"

The crowd stood in the shade to listen to the speechifying.

General W. L. D. Ewing and the Honorable John Posey, both of whom were running for the legislature, felt there was no time like July Fourth to give one's best in a political speech. It was one of the best ways to be sure of an audience, too. The candidates, however, neglected a very important point. They did not remember, nor wish, perhaps, to treat the crowd. The crime of this omission grew with the passing of the long, hot minutes when no drinks were forthcoming. There was considerable murmuring among the men of the crowd during the speeches. Each candidate in turn, however, noisily clearing his throat and running a warm forefinger around the damp stock surrounding his uncomfortable neck, got up on a broad oak stump—all that remained of a tree which had started to grow ten years after the Pilgrims landed on the shores of Massachusetts Bay—and said his piece.

It was too hot to be very eloquent. Applause was sparse and unenthusiastic. The audience felt it was a poor excuse for an Independence Day celebration. Times were surely deteriorating if this was the best that could be produced in honor of the most important day in American history. They wished Judge Erasmus from over to Shelbyville would come. He was late. He was slated to read the Declaration of Independence and give a speech, too, but he didn't come . . . and he didn't come . . . and they began to conclude he'd either died of sunstroke on the road or had business elsewhere.

Jack Johnston and his friends had another firecracker and it was more interesting to watch what they were going to do with it than to listen to fat, old General Ewing, or timid Mr. Posey give their reasons for wanting to have a seat in the legislature. And still neither man treated for drinks. The charge exploded, the crowd cheered. The speeches ended abruptly. The crowd looked for more entertainment.

"Hey, Abe! Where's Abe Lincoln? Let's get Abe to give us a speech! Law, he kin talk better'n ary one of them two. Come on, Abe, it's your turn now. They never treated for drinks, Abe, so you get up and lay it into 'em proper, boy!"

Abe grinned. If there was anything he loved, it was a chance to talk when people were primed for listening. His mind went completely blank, however, trying to think what he would say in his first speech, if they really wanted him to get up.

"Come on, you old river rat!" yelled Oliver Easton. "Give us a speech!"

"Speech! Speech! Speech!" chanted the crowd, delighted to have some fun after the dull orations were over. They all knew Abe Lincoln, who lived out on the Sangamon River, southwest of Decatur. They yelled again when he unfolded his length from under the oak where he had been sitting in the shade, batting flies. He wiped his brow and rubbed the palms of his hands on the seat of his pants and loped on his long legs to the stump. The words of Oliver Easton—river rat—had given him his idea.

He stepped up on the stump and stood tall above the crowd, who grinned up at him in anticipation.

He looked amiably down at them.

"Ladies and gentlemen," he began quietly, not shouting to be heard, and they hushed the children and the dogs so they could hear him. "My friends, as you know, I am unaccustomed to public speaking, so I trust that you will bear with me and not laugh if I should break down in my speech or forget my thoughts, what I have of them. And I beg of you, I'm a po-o-o-or man—*I* can't treat the crowd!" He paused and the people cheered and laughed and assured him he wouldn't have to treat.

And so Abe started. He praised the words of the two speakers who had preceded him, praised them with eloquence and kindness, as if they had been the finest orators since Cicero. With the amenities out of the way, he straightened, hitched up his breeches, stood a little taller.

"It is my opinion," he went on, earnestness in his eyes, "that Illinois is headed for a magnificent future. She is only just beginning to realize what she may become, with industry and diligence, in the years ahead. Illinois is rich in land and in timber and in waters full of fish, rivers waiting for navigation to bring commerce to our doorsteps. You may prefer to travel by the new railroads which are coming in, I hear, and send your goods by that route, but it is the *water-*

ways, in the final analysis, which are part of the state's endowment and part of her route to prosperity. Develop your rivers, ladies and gentlemen, make them safe for navigation, and you have a means of bringing wealth to the very doors of the people! (Cheers)

"I live on the Sangamon River, ladies and gentlemen, on one of the prettiest stretches of that river I've seen in my brief stay in this fair state, but in this short space of time I can see how the Sangamon can bring commerce into the very heart of the nation and of the state. The river connects directly with the Illinois, and the Illinois with the Mississippi, and, as you well know, the Mississippi is the direct highway to New Orleans, the Atlantic Ocean, and the markets of the world.

"Now, the River Sangamon is not always navigable," Abe went on seriously, and the people hung on his words. "Driftwood and timber lying in the waters obstruct the channel, yet if this were properly cleared and the river straightened, it would be made navigable to the mouth of the South Fork, I make no doubt, and at an expense much less than that of building a railroad. Think of it—you good citizens of Decatur, and those of Springfield and other communities rising rapidly in Illinois—you would have the markets of New Orleans and the products of Europe sent to that port, available right here on the banks of the Sangamon!"

The crowd cheered again, grinning broadly. This was meaty stuff and they loved it.

"More, more," they shouted.

Abe smiled happily down at them. All his life, it seemed to him at that moment, he had been waiting for acclaim like this. But cannily he decided against prolonging his speech. Better to quit while they still wanted more, than to overdo it.

"Speaking of the richness of Illinois," he went on, a puckish grin quirking the corners of his mouth. "It reminds me of what I heard before we came here. Mighty nigh discouraged my father and me from ever coming to a land as all-fired rich as that! Why, they told us that corn and wheat grew so fast and tall that when they headed up, they broke over of their own weight, and as for watermelons, listen to this!

"I heard tell that there was a man who planted watermelons, and the soil was so fertile the vines grew so rapidly that, as the melons were developing, they were dragged along the ground so fast they wore all the rinds off, on one side, clear to the heart-meat. And there was a boy one time who went in to steal one of those watermelons, but before he could ever break it loose from the vine, I'll swear, it had dragged him along at such a pace he was bruised and sore, and had to give up! He was in bed for a week with his injuries, besides! That, my friends, is what Illinois's reputation is for wealth and rich-ness!"

He paused and let the crowd roar. He stood there on the stump, his hands hanging awkwardly from his sleeves, and grinned and then bowed in courtly fashion.

"Fellow citizens," he said, "I shall now conclude."

"Hey, Abe," yelled one of his new admirers. "Looks like Judge Erasmus ain't comin'. How's about you readin' that there Declaration of Independence to us? Don't hardly seem right to have a Fourth of July without it."

Abe was startled, and then he was pleased.

"Mr. Renshaw," he called over the heads of the crowd to the owner of the store. "Can I have the loan of your copy of the Declaration?" Abe was pretty sure he knew it by heart, but he didn't want to take any chances on a thing as important as that.

"Sure can, Abe, and I'd admire to hear you read it."

Abe took the paper which Renshaw handed him, the prized copy of the Declaration of Independence which always hung on the wall back of the counter. Abe stepped back on the stump of the tree which had been a good-sized old tree when the Revolution was being fought. He cleared his voice. His tones grew solemn with the solemnity he always felt when he said the words which made America free.

" 'We hold these truths to be self-evident,' " he began slowly, saying the words so that everyone could hear and understand. He did not raise his voice, yet they all heard because they listened, " 'that all men are created equal; that they are endowed by their Creator with certain inalienable rights; that among these are life, liberty, and the pursuit of happiness. . . .' "

The crowd was still, and even Jack and the boys ceased their rascality in firing off powder charges to scare the girls. The words stood out in full clarity in the hot July sunshine. High in the bright blue sky a turkey buzzard soared on motionless wings. Down in the dust of the road a rattlesnake slid across, leaving an undulant trail, and nobody saw it before the snake eased off toward the drying weeds.

" '. . . when a long train of abuses and usurpations pursuing invariably the same object, evinces a design to reduce them to absolute despotism, it is their right, it is their duty, to throw off such government. . . . we do . . . solemnly publish and declare that these united colonies are, and of right ought to be, free and independent states . . . and for the support of this declaration, with a firm reliance on the protection of Divine Providence, we mutually pledge to each other our lives, our fortunes, and our sacred honor. . . .' "

There was a rapt moment of silence, while the turkey buzzard soared and the rattlesnake vanished among the parched ragweeds and a small yellow dog vigorously scratched its left ear. . . . Then the applause broke forth in a storm of approval. All those fine words —they were what every man there would have said if he had known the right ones to say to express how he felt, being an American.

Abe stepped down from the stump and handed the precious document back to James Renshaw.

"I declare, Abe Lincoln," Renshaw said, somewhat in awe, "I never knew them words could be so all-fired movin'. I like to cried, just listenin' to you readin' em!"

Abe's kinfolk beamed in sudden, startled pride at how their Abe was being lauded by the crowd. Dennis clapped him on the back. John Hanks shook his hand, grinning, and then gave way to his brother William, and Jack Johnston stared at Abe as if he were suddenly a stranger, not the fellow who shared his loft bed every night.

"Gosh!" exclaimed Jack in awe. "That there Abe Lincoln's *kin* to me!"

"He is?" said one of his friends. "He's some bully o-rator ain't he?"

CHAPTER TWENTY-ONE

THE ILLINOIS summer dragged on, long and hot. After a thunderstorm had soaked the black earth out in the sod-corn fields, the cornstalks could almost be seen to grow a foot in the humidity between one morning and the next. At night the aroma of the green corn leaves came richly, almost rankly, on the thick, damp, warm air. It was almost too hot to sleep, some nights, until after midnight, when a cooler wind came up and blew across the gently rolling prairie to the cabin on the rise above the river.

When the corn was in the milk, Sarah cooked sweet corn for dinner and threw the well-gnawed cobs to the eager pigs, who champed them down and rooted about for more. Abe and Dennis and Jack thought they could sit and eat roastin' ears until the Day of Judgment, the corn was so good, dripping with butter and sprinkled with salt. And when the watermelons ripened, it was even better than the sweet-corn season, though the two seasons actually overlapped.

The mosquitoes were bad. The rains left standing water in the low places, and plenty of mosquitoes were hatched. They got to be as bad as the flies that summer, and that was saying a good deal! The children in the Lincoln family were sick with summer complaint, and, for a time, Sarah and Tilda despaired of little John Hall's life, weakened as he was by the attacks. He couldn't keep his food down and grew thin and pale. Tilda sat for hours fanning away the flies, and now and then weeping softly at how terrible he looked, wept with the fear of losing her first-born.

Harriet Hanks was ill, too, and even the grownups had sick spells from food which didn't taste quite right in the hot weather, for there was no way of keeping foods fresh, not even a deep well into which milk and butter could be lowered. A thunderstorm could do more than sour milk, Dennis grumbled from his bed, unable to keep any food down while his system worked off the poison.

Abe didn't feel like eating much, and, since it was too hot to work very hard, he lay in the shade back of the cabin, batting flies and mosquitoes, and wished he was some place where it was more comfortable, though he couldn't figure where. The heat made the corn grow, if men could stand it. A fellow broke out in a perspiration if he merely turned over, and it fairly ran off him in streams when he was out laying fence.

By August, people in the neighborhood were down with the ague. There was hardly a well family anywhere. Malaria had taken hold, and husband, wife, or children, or all of them at once, felt the shaking which heralded a spell of chills, when no amount of covers on the hottest day could warm their shivering bones, followed by a burning fever. Then it would quit for a day, and, until they knew better, folk would feel it was finished and they were well, till the next bout of shaking and shivering and burning would come on, regularly as the calendar.

Tom Lincoln came down with it; so did Sarah, and Tilda and Squire Hall. It was up to Elizabeth to manage the household, until she came down with it, too. Then Abe and Dennis took over, best they could. There wasn't much to do. Nobody felt like eating; they only wanted cool water to drink. Abe didn't think it was exactly safe to take water from the river, though it was so close and everyone had been drinking from it ever since they had moved to Macon County. But now the river was so low and scummed with green, and the water was so warm, Abe didn't like the look of it. He lugged water from the spring, over back of the Warnicks'. He perspired so much in the process, however, that he vowed, joking, as he brought the buckets of cold water in, that he'd turned it salty with all that sweat dripping off him. The cold spring water tasted wonderful to parched throats.

The next time Abe went to Renshaw's Store in Decatur, he bought a couple of bottles of *Barks*, which James Renshaw swore was the best thing in the world for shakes.

"It's got quinine beat a mile," he averred, "and costs less, too. You take these here bottles of *Barks* home and see that your folks take it regular, and they'll feel better mighty quick."

"What's in it?" asked Abe, uncorking a bottle and sniffing the strong aroma rising from it.

"Well, don't you dast tell your paw, because he's so down on quinine, thinkin' it's too costly and dangerous to boot, but *Barks* is mere a mixture of quinine and whiskey. Now, don't tell your paw, or he'll never tech it, cause he don't hold with whiskey, either, I just recollected. But if you just tell him it's a fine elixir that'll cure the shakes, he'll be the better for it!"

Barks did wonders for the Lincolns and their kin—though the attacks came on, they were much less severe—and Abe was frequently sent for more bottles of the wonderful medicine.

"You oughtn't to take too much, Paw," warned Abe. "It's mighty strong stuff!"

"Don't you tell me what-all to do," blustered Tom, after a swig of *Barks*, wiping his mouth daintily. "This here medicine has done brought me out of the yawnin' grave, and I don't aim to quit takin' it till come frost and the ague's left for the season!"

A killing frost on September twenty-fifth cut down the nettles and jewelweeds in the river bottoms, knocked down the mosquitoes and flies and browned the ripening corn leaves. Folk who had survived the sickly season began to feel better. After the brief cold spell, October blossomed out as beautifully as any autumn could be—Illinois at its best, minus mosquitoes, flies, ticks, and the shakes of malaria. Life began to be good again. Tom Lincoln, who had been so disgusted with Illinois during the summer, gave up talking about leaving. Abe, who wanted to get away again, somewhere, anywhere, stayed on, undecided in his own mind as to what he should do.

Tom Lincoln reveled in the long, lovely, golden autumn. It was even finer than autumn in Indiana, superior to Kentucky, where autumns lasted long and beautifully. Day after day, the sun shone kindly and dreamily over the ripening landscape. There was little rain, and the river was low and slow, a shining stream on which the golden leaves of the elms in the bottoms drifted like a fleet of yellow boats, on, on, to wherever it is that autumn leaves drift.

Papaws ripened. Red haws were abundant. Sarah Lincoln made red-haw jelly, using precious loaf sugar and turning out a splendid, crystal-ruby confection to be saved for special company or when the circuit rider came to dinner. Jack and Abe were busy cutting rails for John Hanks as the autumn days passed. Wild geese went south in long V's and lines. Ducks passed over, or paused on prairie sloughs. There were huge flights of whistling curlews and plover, and their voices came down out of the night to the lone cabins on the Illinois prairie.

It was time to harvest the corn and stack the fodder, but aside from piling up the pumpkins outside the barn, where they glinted in a burnished orange heap in the warm sunshine of late October, everything was left untouched in the fields. Evidently, concluded Tom, Illinois autumns were long, if they ever ended before spring, and there would be time enough.

Abe got busy on an order of a thousand fence rails for Major Warnick, for which he would receive two dollars and fifty cents, and he wasn't at home very much of the time. Anyway, it was up to Tom Lincoln and John Hanks, on their respective farms, to say when it was time to cut fodder and get the corn in for the winter. In the meanwhile, Sarah and the girls cut up the pumpkins and dried them for winter.

December came. It was considerably cooler, it is true, and the leaves were all down, but the weather was still fine, and there had been little rain, so the fields were dry and the corn was curing nicely.

"Really ought to get that corn in the barn," commented Tom one lazy December day when there wasn't a cloud in the pale blue bowl of sky, and crows were talking in the woods, their voices carrying far in the stillness. "Might be we'll get a snow soon. Time for it, leastwise."

And suddenly, the snow came. On Christmas Day, which was like any other day in the crowded Lincoln cabin above the lazy-winding Sangamon River, the morning broke gray and lowering, with a gnawing wind out of the northeast. There were feathers of white fluttering briskly on that wind. By noon the feathers were no longer fluttering. They were no longer featherlike. They were small, frozen pellets which were flung almost horizontally on a roaring wind that had veered to the northwest and was bringing with it a genuine blizzard.

Abe happened to be home that day. He and Tom and Jack plunged out into the wind, which cut like thin knives, and raced to get in the stock. The horses were standing with their tails to the storm, heads lowered, legs braced against the wind, their backs whitened. The cow was urged to the barn, and the pigs were rounded up and put inside.

The blizzard did not end with the coming of night. Darkness was a howling demon, screaming out of the north, blowing the blinding curtain of snow so that it heaped high wherever it met obstructions. Houses, barns, fences, trees and the drifts in turn were carved by the wind into fantastic shapes. The storm still raged the next day and the next night, and not until the third day did the wind abate and the snow stop. The clouds cracked and let out a blinding sun in a blue sky, and folk squinted painfully when they came out of their houses into a winter world.

The door of the Lincoln cabin was blocked with a drift. Bundled to the eyes, Abe and Dennis pushed out into the zero cold and plunged through drifts up to their waists to get to the barn. The animals were all alive, but hungry. They met their rescuers with reproachful lows and whinnies and grunts. Abe forked down some hay. He and the other men would have to get into the field and dig some fodder. Just now he needed the shovel to break a path between barn and house and privy and smokehouse, so they wouldn't be shut in so tightly.

At last he went back to the cabin where Tom sat nearest the fire, with the whole family huddled around him. This seemed to be the only warm spot left in the whole world. Even the far end of the cabin was chill, in spite of the blazing logs.

"Paw," Abe announced, stamping off the snow, "we got to get out and dig some fodder from the field. The animals haven't much to eat but hay, and that won't do them long. Squire and Jack, you come with me and Dennis and help get some fodder out!"

"Won't need all of us," mumbled Jack, comfortable where he was. "I reckon you and Squire here can cut enough for today, and I'll take a turn tomorrow, if the snow ain't melted off by then. I look for it to go off fast as it come."

Abe, in vast impatience at the indolence of his kin, turned on his heel.

"Come on, Jack!" he ordered.

"Do I have to?" whined Jack.

"You do!" said Abe with no hesitation, and Jack reluctantly came, well bundled against the razoring wind.

The cornfield was so deep in snow that only the tips of the stalks still jutted out. It was a job to get at them, because the snow had iced them. Besides, the crust wasn't strong enough to hold up the weight of a man, and the workers broke through and were up to their waists in snow and ice crystals part of the time. The snow got down into their boots and soaked their feet and legs. The wind cut their faces until they were red and stinging. When their noses began to lose all sensation, Abe grabbed a handful of snow and rubbed his nose and Jack's, though the latter yelled with the pain of it.

"Oh, shut up, Jack," said Abe impatiently. "It hurts my face as much as it does yours. You don't want your nose to freeze off, do you? That'd be a whole lot worse. Now hurry up, load that fodder and the corn on the sled and let's go in. We got enough for the day, anyway, and maybe it won't be so bad tomorrow."

It was worse than ever the next day. More snow fell during the night. In fact, it seemed to snow almost every day, and pretty soon the Lincoln family couldn't see the cornstalks, except for an occasional dried tassel jutting out where the wind had scooped a hollow around it. It was getting to be a monstrous job to dig out the fodder and bring in the ripe yellow ears of corn, which should have been brought in months ago, when the weather was still good. Grimly, Abe and the other men of the family went out, day after day, and dug enough fodder and corn to keep themselves and the animals from starving. Sarah cooked dried pumpkin chips as many ways as she could think of; the family lived on pumpkin and corn and salt pork for months.

Every day the paths had to be broken out again. Every day the drifts grew higher, until they were fifteen feet deep on the prairie. One day a rise in temperature came, and with it a miserable, gray, icy rain, which glazed everything and made a crust on the snow. The trees were iced and many broke. Those that still stood creaked in the wind and glittered dazzlingly in the sunshine. Birds perching for the night found their tails frozen fast and flew off awkwardly without them.

It was a difficult time for the wild creatures. The crust was hard enough now to hold up both men and beasts. The wolves prowled over the mountainous drifts, hunting, hunting, their hunger-howls coming mournfully and eerily over the desolate white country. The deer, which had floundered helplessly in the soft snow and could not find tender twigs to browse on, now could not stand up on the icy crust which would have lifted them high enough to reach for more twigs. The deer were starving; they were weak; they were helpless. The wolves, at least, fared well for a time, until most of the deer were gone, and the last were only skin and bone and haunted eyes.

The quail starved. The seeds which they were accustomed to use for food were buried deeply beneath the drifts. The wolves caught the quail, too, and foxes picked them out of sheltering drifts at night. The wild turkeys were gaunt; they were never again as abundant in the Illinois Country after the Winter of the Deep Snow.

CHAPTER TWENTY-TWO

Abraham lincoln thought he could not endure another day of it. Still, he could at least get out, could leave the crowded, smelly, uncomfortable cabin where the children cried most of the time and fought with each other. They all had the bold-hives and endless colds; and Squire Hall and Dennis Hanks spit and argued, and Tom Lincoln coughed and hacked with a misery in his throat.

There were too many women in one small cabin, and pretty soon even the patient and forbearing Sarah Lincoln snapped at her daughters. Elizabeth and Tilda got into a bitter argument over whose children had a better right to the best trundle bed and wouldn't speak to each other for a week. Matilda, besides, railed at Squire Hall, calling him lazy and shiftless in such acid tones that he up and slapped her. Matilda burst into tears, Tom roared at Squire for striking a woman, even if she was his wife, Sarah screamed at them all and then burst into tears herself. The five children, seeing their betters in such a state, added their own howls to the din. Tom, in the rocking chair, rocked on the hound-dog's tail, and the dog yelped and jumped up so awkwardly that he upset the poker, which fell over and hit Tom's sore toe. Abe, his face white with withheld anger, flung open the door and strode out.

"I'm going over to Major Warnick's to finish that order of fence rails," he said tersely. "May not be back for a couple days." Wish it was never, he fumed, plunging into the snow.

Outdoors, even though the cold cut his face and the snow was a dazzle that made him squint, it was open and free and quiet and splendid. There were no screaming children and quarreling women, no coughing old men and arguing kinfolk, no smells of dirty clothes that couldn't be washed until spring, no reek of winter underwear that got stronger as the months went by, no stale odor of fried pork, and the sickening-sweet smell of onion syrup which Elizabeth always had on hand for her children's unending colds. He was outdoors and free. He much preferred being cold and snow-dazzled to being cooped up a minute longer inside that house back there where a curl of blue smoke rose with deceiving calmness into the sunshine.

Abe was big and heavy, but the crust was thick enough to hold his weight. He went down the bluff trail to the Sangamon, then slanted across the ice and snow covering its winding length, heading toward Major Warnick's big house, set back a distance from the river.

He didn't know how it happened when it had been so cold for so long, but somehow, there was a spot of ice, eaten out by moving water beneath, perhaps, which caved in under him. Abe Lincoln suddenly found himself knee deep in the bitterest ice water he had ever known. It was so cold it almost paralyzed his legs from the knees down, and they ached with an intolerable pain. Fortunately, the river was still low from the long autumn of dry weather; otherwise, he would have been in it to his waist or more.

It was an effort to get his legs out, first one, then the other. He stood with them dripping a moment and then freezing in the zero wind. His pants-legs froze solid about his legs, and he hated to think of the ice forming inside his boots, around his feet, stiffening his socks into immobile casings. He'd have to get to a house, fast, while he could still move his legs. He was closer to Warnicks' than to his own home, so he headed in that direction.

His feet were hurting badly as he slipped and awkwardly worked his way up the embankment on the other side, holding on to branches of bushes and pulling himself along, trying to get a purchase on the crust. By the time he had reached the top, he couldn't feel his feet any more, which was a mercy, he figured. But it was getting hard to move his legs, and he had almost half a mile to go. He stumbled and fell often, and cut his wrists on the crust. Pretty soon, with the big house in sight, he simply couldn't get up on his numb, freezing feet again, and he had to crawl painfully the last few rods.

Eliza Warnick chanced to come to the door to throw a scrap to the dog on the porch when she saw the apparition dragging itself over the snow.

"For the love of heaven, Abe Lincoln, what's happened?" she cried. "William!" she called to her husband. "Come quick! It's Abe Lincoln. He's hurt."

Major Warnick and his sons streamed forth and, with a good deal of racket and advice, got Abe into the house.

"Pull off his boots, quick," cried Mrs. Warnick. "Jim, go get me a bucket of snow, fast as you can. Now—see if you can peel off those socks. Will—oh, the poor boy, let me do it—look at the ice on those poor feet of his, blue with cold, too. You must have fallen into the river, Abe!"

"Yes, ma'am," admitted Abe, warming up enough to talk. "Silliest thing I ever did, but you'd never think there could be weak ice on a day as cold as this, now would you?" He smiled engagingly, then winced at the pain of his feet.

"No, I wouldn't," said Mrs. Warnick briefly, "but seems you found it. Now then," she grasped the bucket of snow and plunged Abe's feet into it. He yelled.

"Go ahead and yell if you want," she said, briskly rubbing the feet in the snow. "But you'll yell harder if you have to have your feet cut off. It'll be a mercy if they aren't already frozen beyond help. Tommy," she added, "it's your turn. Go out for more snow!" She applied a fresh dose and Abe, knowing it had to be done, withheld his groans. Already his feet were coming to; he could feel them again—and they were hurting worse than anything ever hurt in his life.

When the snow applications satisfied Mrs. Warnick, she got a towel and wiped his big feet tenderly. She examined the toes for signs of damage and shook her head over the way they looked.

"William, help Abe to the bed and put that old tow sack under his feet." She went to the chest and got out a bottle of oil.

"This here is rabbit oil," she said, pouring some in her hand and rubbing it over his feet with special attention to the swollen toes.

"Now you lay there and rest."

Before he knew it, Abe was asleep. The Warnick children tiptoed in and looked at him, covered up with their mother's good quilt.

"Don't you dast to waken him," their mother warned. "It's a mercy he ain't froze to death, and I'll be mightily surprised if he keeps all his toes, let alone his feet. He'll have to stay here till he can walk again. Sam, you run to Mr. Lincoln's house and tell them Abe's here—and will be till I say he can leave."

Two weeks with the Warnicks was as near a vacation as Abe could want. He was too sick to work, but he was well enough to sit up and read. He ate well, told stories to the children, helped Mrs. Warnick card wool or break hominy; he had a lovely time, especially with Major Warnick's books. It made him shudder to think of what it would have been like if he had been laid up in his own house.

The day finally came, however, when he was able to go out into the cold again and attack the order of fence rails of which Major Warnick had reminded him with clocklike regularity.

When the job was done at last, Abe went home. The snow was still thick, deeper than ever; it snowed every day for two months that winter. He found the children all sick, and Tom's cough no better. There was a strained look on Sarah's face, but she greeted Abe affectionately, kissed him and inquired about his feet.

"Cousin John was in yesterday," commented Tom Lincoln from his seat by the fireplace. "Said he was in Decatur and ran across a fellow name of Denton Offutt from over to Springfield, or some such place. Says this Offutt wants a couple fellows to take his flatboat of produce down to New Orleans, come spring. All this snow, there'll be a big run off when the breakup does come. John, he says he told this Offutt that maybe you'd relish the trip, and since you done had one already, you'd be expert at it."

Abe Lincoln stood there, listening to his father open the door of adventure and escape to him. Tom Lincoln had never opened much of anything to his eager son, but now—he was actually offering him a trip to New Orleans. New Orleans! The memory of that beautiful, warm, exciting city, which was full of flowers and fine people even in January, blotted out for a moment the deadly reality of the cramped, ugly, smelly cabin and the endless and never-melting drifts of the Winter of the Deep Snow. New Orleans.

"Oh, Lord," he prayed inside himself, "this is it! Let me get the job! I've got to get that job!"

Stout, cigar-smoking, paunchy, braggardly little Mr. Denton Offutt finally found the Lincoln cabin. His bony horse picked its way out the Decatur-Springfield road one briefly thawing day, and he talked to Abraham Lincoln.

"I'll guarantee to have a good big flatboat ready and loaded when you come to Springfield," the little man promised grandiosely. "You kin tell when to come by how the Sangamon River looks. Soon's the snow goes off, the river'll rise considerable, and then's when we got to get on our way, because that river drops fast and we cain't get through some spots with a big boat less'n the water's floodin' pretty high. You watch, and when it's time, you haste over to Springfield. Ask anyone where to find me. I'm well known thereabouts, though you'll more'n likely find me in the Buckhorn Tavern."

The little man grinned, taking a gold toothpick out of his pocket and digging at a fiber of meat between his yellow teeth.

"I hear tell your cousin John Hanks might come along. Got anyone else who can go?"

"Maybe Jack Johnston, my stepbrother, will want to," suggested Abe, his heart singing.

"Fine, fine," said Mr. Offutt, pulling on his dogskin gloves.

"What you goin' to pay?" grunted Tom Lincoln from his chair. In the excitement of the trip itself, Abe hadn't thought of asking what the pay might be. Pay was unimportant. It was getting away which was the vital thing. He was going to get out of the wilderness at last.

"Oh, the pay, the pay," said Mr. Offutt. "Why, I reckon ten dollars a month'll do the trick. Is that satisfactory, Mr. Lincoln?" He looked coldly at Tom Lincoln.

"Reckon it is," Tom grunted. "Now that Abe's come of age, he's likely too big to bring his pay home to his pappy like he used to do;

but leastwise, I still got rights to Jack's pay."

"You can have mine, too," said Abe distantly, embarrassed at Tom's talk. "I don't want it."

"I'll take you up on that, Son," said Tom more cheerfully. "After this awful winter and the sickly summer afore that, I don't aim to stay here another year. I'm goin' to move south again, and I'll need all the cash money I can lay hands to."

"Good day, gentlemen," said Denton Offutt briskly, not looking at Tom Lincoln, and shaking hands with the tall young giant who had to bend his head to get through the door as he went out with him. "I'll see you at Springfield, come the breakup."

"You sure will!" Abe Lincoln grinned in anticipation.

But that night it snowed again. The next day it was still snowing. There was a blizzard three days later. In vast disgust and impatience, Abe looked at the endless miles of snow and hated it with every ounce of hate in his whole long resentful body. He hoped he would never, never see snow again when this went off. And it couldn't go off any too soon to suit him.

But a week later, it was still snowing. Abe paced. He worked outdoors as much as possible, getting the last of the fodder out of the depleted, snowed-under field. There was only one thing in the world he wanted: the thaw.

Figuring that when the breakup did come, the road to Springfield would be too muddy for any use, John Hanks, Jack and Abe passed the time of waiting by felling a big cottonwood and burning and hacking it out to make a long, heavy, round-bottomed canoe. They would go by water to Springfield.

But the ice seemed thicker than ever on the Sangamon, their highway to escape. The drifts on land were interminable, winter unending.

CHAPTER TWENTY-THREE

Night arched in silence over the snow. It was very still, still with the quietness of winter, waiting . . . waiting . . . for some indication that its time might be nearing an end. The sky during the night had cleared and was deep black. Against this darkness the stars flashed with their old winter brilliance, yet, as the night moved on, the winter constellations were sinking toward the west and spring stars rose in the east. The wind, which had been bitterly northwest when night came on, had died, and a new wind sprang up, gentle, urgent, chilly, but ineffably sweet and damp, blowing from the south over the miles of vast snowdrifts and frozen rivers of the Illinois Country.

Shortly after midnight on that night in late February, the whole landscape lay expectant. The dark forest trees stood massive on the horizon. The cleared fields were smooth and curving white. Down along the course of the winding Sangamon River the ice locking it began softly to murmur and mutter within itself. Strange booming sounds came from its depths. The black water under the ice gnawed at the hard layer above it, eating it out, crystal by crystal, and dissolving them silently in the secret darkness of the river night. Broad and dark and full of portent, the world of old snow and timeless sky and cold trees, and the few lone small cabins jutting out of the acres of snow seemed held in the breathless grip of a dream, waiting.

In the loft, where he was sleeping with Jack Johnston, Abe Lincoln stirred. He was quite suddenly wide-awake, and he was sure something had roused him. It was something . . . something he had been waiting for—waiting, it seemed to him, for an eternity of time. As he listened, an unaccountable excitement made his heart hammer.

Then he heard it . . . a small sound . . . almost musical, the thin, liquid voice of spring . . . drip . . . drip . . . drip.

The eaves were dripping! The wind had turned at last. The snow was melting. The thaw—the thaw had begun. *The thaw!*

Abraham Lincoln, with an old buffalo robe over him, lay back on the rustling cornshuck tick and grinned into the cold darkness, listening to those beautiful drips. It had come! It wouldn't be very long now before the water would be open and he and Jack and John Hanks could get started down the river, bound for Springfield and the place where Denton Offutt's boat was waiting, to get aboard and head grandly south, down the Sangamon, the Illinois and the Mississippi, to New Orleans.

A warm feeling of unutterable joy flooded over him at the thought of it. It would be like coming alive again to throw off the intolerable shackles of the Winter of the Deep Snow, to break away, now that he was of age and no longer bound to his father, of going adventuring out of the wilderness, down those beckoning three rivers, south!